ESSENTIAL SKILLS
FOR GCSE
Biology

Dan Foulder

HODDER
EDUCATION
AN HACHETTE UK COMPANY

Although every effort has been made to ensure that website addresses are correct at time of going to press, Hodder Education cannot be held responsible for the content of any website mentioned in this book. It is sometimes possible to find a relocated web page by typing in the address of the home page for a website in the URL window of your browser.

Hachette UK's policy is to use papers that are natural, renewable and recyclable products and made from wood grown in well-managed forests and other controlled sources. The logging and manufacturing processes are expected to conform to the environmental regulations of the country of origin.

Orders: please contact Bookpoint Ltd, 130 Park Drive, Milton Park, Abingdon, Oxon OX14 4SE. Telephone: +44 (0)1235 827827. Fax: +44 (0)1235 400401. Email: education@bookpoint.co.uk. Lines are open from 9 a.m. to 5 p.m., Monday to Saturday, with a 24-hour message answering service. You can also order through our website: www.hoddereducation.co.uk

ISBN: 978 1 5104 6000 3

© Dan Foulder 2019

First published in 2019 by
Hodder Education,
An Hachette UK Company
Carmelite House
50 Victoria Embankment
London EC4Y 0DZ

www.hoddereducation.co.uk

Impression number 10 9 8 7 6 5 4 3 2 1

Year 2023 2022 2021 2020 2019

Cover photo [tbc]

Illustrations by [tbc]

Typeset by Integra Software Services Pvt. Ltd., Pondicherry, India

Printed by Replika Press Pvt. Ltd., Haryana, India

A catalogue record for this title is available from the British Library.

Contents

Paper 2 with Exam-style questions and answers can be found online at
www.hoddereducation.co.uk/EssentialSkillsBiology.

How to use this book

Welcome to *Essential Skills for GCSE Biology*. This book covers the major UK exam boards for Science: AQA, Edexcel (including Edexcel International GCSE), OCR 21st Century and Gateway, WJEC/Eduqas and CCEA. Where exam board requirements differ, these specifics are flagged. This book is designed to help you go beyond the subject-specific knowledge and develop the underlying essential skills needed to do well in GCSE Science. These skills include Maths, Literacy, and Working Scientifically, which now have an increased focus.

- The Maths chapter covers the five key areas required by the government, with different Biology-specific contexts. In your Biology exams, questions testing Maths Skills make up 10% of the marks available.
- The Literacy chapter will help you learn how to answer extended response questions. You will be expected to answer at least one of these per paper, depending on your specification and they are usually worth six marks.
- The Working Scientifically chapter covers the four key areas that are required in all GCSE sciences.
- The Revision chapter explains how to improve the efficiency of your revision using retrieval practice techniques.
- The Exam Skills chapter explains way of improving your performance in the actual exam.

To help you practise your skills, there is an exam-style paper at the end of the book, with another available online at www.hoddereducation.co.uk/EssentialSkillsBiology. While they are not designed to be accurate representations of any particular specification or exam paper, they are made up of exam-style questions and will require you to put your maths, literacy and practical skills into action.

Key features

In addition to Key term and Tip boxes throughout the book, there are several other features designed to help you develop your skills.

 Worked examples

These boxes contain questions where the working required to reach the correct answer has been shown.

 Expert commentary

These sample extended responses are provided with expert commentary, a mark and an explanation of why it was awarded.

 Guided questions

These boxes guide you in the right direction, so you can work towards solving the question yourself.

 Peer assessment

These activities ask you to use a mark scheme to assess the sample answer and justify the score you have given.

 Practice questions

These exam-style questions will test your understanding of the subject.

 Improve the answer

These activities ask you to rewrite the sample answer to improve it and earn full marks.

Answers to all questions can be found at the back of the book. These are fully worked solutions with step-by-step calculations included. Answers for the second online exam-style paper can also be found online at www.hoddereducation.co.uk/EssentialSkillsBiology.

★ **Flags like this one will inform you of any specific exam board requirements.**

1 Maths

Maths is an important part of GCSE Biology, but you do not need to be too wary of the skills you need to know and apply. Remember that these are all skills you will be using in GCSE maths – just in a different context, namely biology.

Common maths questions in biology include drawing graphs, calculating means, working out probabilities from genetic crosses and determining rates of reaction. All of these examples – along with many others – are covered in this section.

» Units

Scientific quantities are measured using units. Units are very important in biology. Without them, numerical values are often meaningless, and leaving them out will cost you marks in the exam. You should ensure that you use appropriate units across all calculations and data handling.

A range of units are used in biology. Whenever possible, you should use the internationally recognised SI units. The table below summarises common SI units which may feature in the biology exams.

Table 1.1 Base units in GCSE Biology

Measurement	Unit	Abbreviation
mass	kilogram	kg
length	metre	m
time	second	s
temperature	degree Celsius	°C
amount of substance	mole	mol
luminous intensity	candela	cd

As it would be inappropriate to give the mass of something like a plant 'cutting' in kilograms (it is far too big a unit), biologists also tend to use smaller (submultiple) and larger (multiple) units in calculations. The common ones are shown in the table below.

Table 1.2 Common submultiple and multiple units

Prefix	Symbol	Meaning	Example
micro-	µ	one millionth	$1\,\mu m = \dfrac{1}{1\,000\,000}$
milli-	m	one thousandth	$1\,ms = \dfrac{1}{1000}$
centi-	c	one hundredth	$1\,cm = \dfrac{1}{100}$
kilo-	k	one thousand	$1\,kg = 1000$
Mega-	M	one million	$1\,Mm = 1\,000\,000\,m$ or $1000\,km$

» Arithmetic and numerical computation

Expressions in decimal form

Decimal numbers are those with digits to the right of the decimal point (.), for example 5.1 or 0.9.

Decimal numbers can be rounded up or down for simpler values and calculations. This rounding can be done as follows:

- Values ending in 0.5 or greater (0.6, 0.7, 0.8, 0.9) should be rounded up, for example 0.68 could be rounded to 0.7.
- Values ending in 0.4 or below (0.3, 0.2, 0.1) should be rounded down, for example 0.34 could be rounded to 0.3.

You should ensure that you round using the appropriate number of decimal places (d.p.) in answers to exam questions. This will probably depend on the number of significant figures used in the question (see pages 13–14 for more information on significant figures) or on the data provided.

In practical questions involving measurements, your answers should not have more decimal places than the least accurate measurement. For example, if a ruler is used to measure the area of the sides of a cube to the nearest 0.1 cm, the surface area (cm^2) and volume (cm^3) calculated using this value should not be given to more than one decimal place.

While most values have an exact number of decimal places, others might have recurring decimals (for example $\frac{1}{3}$ = 0.333333333 recurring) or an infinite number of decimal places (like pi – π). These unusual values should always be rounded to the appropriate number of decimal places.

> **Tip**
> Decimal numbers can also often be used to express fractions, for example $\frac{1}{2}$ = 0.5.

> **Key term**
> Decimal places: The number of integers given after a decimal point.

> **Tip**
> If creating results tables in your exam or a required practical, remember that all of the values should have the same number of decimal points.

A Worked example

The volume of a human stomach was estimated as 1.065 litres. Write this volume to the nearest 0.1 litre.

Step 1 As the second decimal place value is 6 you should round up to one decimal place.

Step 2 This gives an answer of: 1.065 litres = 1.1 litres (to the nearest 0.1 litre).

B Guided questions

1   **A root had a diameter of 0.345 cm. Write this diameter to one decimal place.**

    Step 1 The second decimal place is 4, so you should round down.

    Step 2 Root diameter to one decimal place = ...

2   **In an investigation into density of fungal tissue, a digital balance was used to measure the mass of a sample to the nearest 0.01 g. A ruler was used to measure the fungus to determine the volume. The ruler measured to the nearest 0.1 cm. The density in g/cm³ was then calculated.**

    What is the maximum number of decimal places the density should be stated to?

    Step 1 The density was found using two pieces of apparatus, one that was accurate to two decimal places (the balance) and one that was accurate to one decimal place (the ruler). Remember that the calculated density should not use more decimal places than the least accurate piece of apparatus.

    Step 2 Number of decimal places = ...

C Practice questions

3 An investigation into the activity of amylase yielded 6.8736 g of glucose. Write this mass to two decimal places.

4 A food chain had a conversion efficiency of 10.2% between the primary consumer and secondary consumer, and 9.8% between the secondary consumer and the tertiary consumer. How many decimal places should the conversion efficiency of the producers to the primary consumers be given to? Explain your answer.

Expressions in standard form

In biology, we often use very large numbers or very small numbers. For example, the energy that a plant receives from the Sun could be 1 800 000 kJ/m²/yr while a bacterial cell can have a diameter of 0.005 mm. Rather than writing these numbers with many zeros, which can be difficult to read and understand, we can use standard form (also known as scientific notation) to present the numbers more compactly. Here are some examples:

$$10\,000 = 1 \times 10^4$$
$$1000 = 1 \times 10^3$$
$$100 = 1 \times 10^2$$
$$10 = 1 \times 10^1$$
$$0.1 = 1 \times 10^{-1}$$
$$0.01 = 1 \times 10^{-2}$$
$$0.001 = 1 \times 10^{-3}$$
$$0.0001 = 1 \times 10^{-4}$$

The number of zeros translates into a power of 10 when each number is written in standard form. Powers are written as superscript numbers – for example, 10 to the power 2 is written as 10^2 – the small raised number 2 is the power.

A positive power means you multiply by that power of 10. Essentially, this means that you need to multiply by 10 the same number of times as the power. For example, 1×10^3 has the power 3, so we multiply 1 by 10 three times:

$$1 \times 10 \times 10 \times 10 = 1000 = 1 \times 10^3$$

When representing numbers that are smaller than 1 in standard form, you get negative powers (for example 1×10^{-1}). Essentially, this means that you need to divide by 10 the same number of times as the power. For example, 1×10^{-2} has the power -2, so we need to divide 1 by 10 twice:

$$1 \div 10 \div 10 = 0.01 = 1 \times 10^{-2}.$$

> **Tip**
> When multiplying numbers in standard form, add the powers together and multiply the other numbers.

A Worked examples

1 A xylem vessel has a width of 0.072 mm. Write this width in standard form.

   Step 1 We know that $0.01 = 1 \times 10^{-2}$

   Step 2 As the width is 0.072, replace the 1 with 7.2

   Step 3 This gives an answer of $0.072\,mm = 7.2 \times 10^{-2}\,mm$

2 A temperate forest sample site was $2 \times 10^3\,m$ long and $1 \times 10^3\,m$ wide. What is the total area of this sample site?

   When multiplying numbers in standard form, add the powers together and multiply the other numbers.

   $$2 \times 10^3 \times 1 \times 10^3$$
   $$= 2 \times 1 \times 10^{3+3}$$
   $$= 2 \times 10^6\,m^2$$

B Guided questions

Key term

Mean: The mean is a type of average. Means are covered on pages 14–15.

1 A human lung contains 500 million alveoli. The mean volume of one alveolus is 4.2×10^{-3}. What is the total mean volume of all the alveoli in this lung? Give your answer in standard form.

   Step 1 First convert the number of alveoli into standard form:

   500 million = ...

   Step 2 Now multiply the number of alveoli by the mean volume of one alveolus:

   $4.2 \times 10^{-3} \times$ .... = ...

2 A species of bacterium divides every two hours. If there are 10 bacteria in the original population, how many bacteria would there be after 24 hours? Use the equation below and give your answer in standard form:

   Bacterial population = initial bacterial population $\times 2^{\text{number of divisions}}$

   Step 1 Work out how many divisions will occur in 24 hours. Do this by dividing the mean division time by the total time.

   $24 \div 2 = 12$

   Therefore there are 12 divisions in 24 hours.

   Step 2 Substitute the values into the equation.

   Bacterial population $= 10 \times 2^{12} =$ ....

C Practice questions

3 A fungal colony has an estimated mass of 605 000 kg. Give this number in standard form.

4 A nucleus has a diameter of 0.005 mm. Write this number in standard form.

5 A species of bacterium divides every 5 hours. If there are 200 bacteria in the original population, how many bacteria would there be after 30 hours? Use the equation in Guided question 2 and give your answer in standard form.

Fractions, percentages and ratios

Fractions and percentages

A fraction is part of a whole, and is expressed as a whole number divided by another whole number. The number on the top of the fraction is the numerator and the number on the bottom of the fraction is the denominator.

When using fractions, it is good practice to write each fraction in its simplest form, for example $\frac{5}{10}$ could also be written as $\frac{4}{8}$, $\frac{3}{6}$ or $\frac{2}{4}$, however the simplest form is $\frac{1}{2}$ so this should be used.

To find the simplest form of a fraction, divide the numerator and denominator (top number and bottom number) by the same whole number (a common factor), and carry on doing this until you are left with numerators and denominators which cannot be divided further to give whole numbers.

For example, in $\frac{2}{8}$ the numerator and the denominator can both be divided by 2 to give whole numbers, so $\frac{2}{8} = \frac{1}{4}$.

In $\frac{9}{12}$ both the numerator and the denominator can be divided by 3 to give whole numbers, so $\frac{9}{12} = \frac{3}{4}$. 3 and 4 cannot be further divided by the same number to give whole numbers, so $\frac{3}{4}$ is the simplest way of writing this fraction.

Like fractions, percentages represent part of a whole. Unlike fractions, they are expressed in the form of a number followed by the percentage symbol %, which means 'divided by 100' or 'out of 100'. For example: $\frac{1}{4} = \frac{25}{100} = 25\%$.

To convert a fraction into a percentage, divide the numerator (top number) by the denominator (bottom number) and multiply by 100.

> **Key terms**
>
> Fraction: A number which represents part of a whole.
>
> Numerator: The number on the top of the fraction.
>
> Denominator: The number on the bottom of the fraction.
>
> Common factor: A whole number that will divide into both the numerator and denominator of a fraction to give whole numbers.

> **Tip**
> • • • • • • • • • • • • •
> If both the numerator and the denominator are even numbers, then the fraction is not in its simplest form.

A Worked examples

1 **In a drugs trial, 12 out of 36 participants showed an improvement in their symptoms. Write this as a fraction in its simplest form.**

   Step 1 Write 12 out of 36 as a fraction: $\frac{12}{36}$.

   Step 2 Divide both numbers in the fraction by the same number to get whole numbers. Both 12 and 36 are even and therefore have 2 as a factor. Divide them both by 2 to get $\frac{6}{18}$.

   Step 3 Both 6 and 18 are also even, so divide them both by 2 again to get $\frac{3}{9}$.

   Step 4 It is clear that 3 is a common factor of 3 and 9. Divide both of them by 3 to give $\frac{1}{3}$.

   It is not possible to further divide the numerator and the denominator by the same factor to get whole numbers, so the simplest form of the fraction is $\frac{1}{3}$.

2 **An investigation was carried out into the effect of changing NaCl concentration on the mass of a sample of carrot in solution. The sample of carrot lost 3 g of its total mass of 10 g. What percentage of its mass did the carrot lose?**

   Step 1 In this case, the 'whole' is 10 g and the 'part' is 3 g, so the carrot lost $\frac{3}{10}$ of its mass.

   Step 2 To convert this fraction to a percentage, divide the numerator (3) by the denominator (10) and multiply by 100:

   $$\frac{3}{10} \times 100 = 30\%$$

> **Tip**
> • • • • • • • • • • • • •
> If you recognise from the outset that 12 is a factor of 36, a quicker way to do the calculation would be to divide both the numerator and the denominator by their common factor 12:
>
> $$\frac{12}{12} = 1$$
>
> $$\frac{36}{12} = 3$$
>
> therefore $\frac{12}{36} = \frac{1}{3}$

B Guided questions

1   Stocks of cod in the Atlantic declined drastically during the twentieth century. In recent years, cod stocks have begun to recover, however scientists continue to study cod populations carefully. In one particular area, the cod biomass was estimated to have fallen from 2500 tonnes to 1500 tonnes. Represent this new biomass as a fraction of the original biomass. Give your answer in the simplest form.

1500 is the numerator and 2500 is the denominator.

Step 1 This gives the fraction $\frac{1500}{2500}$
This is not the simplest form of this fraction.

Step 2 To find the simplest form of this fraction, divide both numbers by a common factor. The largest common factor of these two numbers is 500.

$$\frac{\text{new biomass}}{\text{original biomass}} = \text{......................}$$

2   In a day, 4000 kJ of light energy from the Sun falls on a plant. The plant converts 52 kJ of this energy into photosynthetic products.

Calculate how efficient this energy transfer is, giving your answer as a percentage.

To calculate the percentage efficiency of this energy transfer, divide the amount of energy in the photosynthetic products by the total energy falling on the plant, and then multiply the answer by 100.

Step 1 Efficiency of energy transfer = ... ÷ .... × 100

Step 2 Efficiency of energy transfer = ...

C Practice questions

3   An investigation was carried out into the transfer of biomass through a moorland ecosystem. The results were used to draw the following food chain.

Calculate the efficiency of the transfers below. In each case, represent your answer as both a percentage and a fraction in its simplest form.

a   the heather and the grouse
b   the grouse and the fox

4   The four bases in DNA are adenine (A), thymine (T), guanine (G) and cytosine (C). A always pairs with T, and C always pairs with G.

In a given sample of DNA, 30% of the bases are thymine. Calculate what percentage of the bases are guanine.

Ratios

A ratio expresses a relationship between quantities. It shows how many of one thing you have relative to how many of one or more other things. In ratios, the numbers are separated by a colon (:).

For example, suppose that when two plants of a certain species are crossed, eight offspring with red petals are produced for every four offspring with purple petals. The ratio of plants with red petals to those with purple petals is therefore 8 : 4.

> **Key term**
>
> Ratio: A way to compare quantities; for example, three apples and four oranges are in the ratio 3 : 4.

Just like with fractions, you should always try to represent ratios in their simplest form. To do this:

- Divide all of the numbers in the ratio by the same number (a common factor).
- Continue doing this until you are left with an expression that cannot be divided further to give whole numbers.
- In the example above, both sides of the ratio can be divided by 4 to give whole numbers. The ratio then becomes 2 red petal plants : 1 purple petal plant.
- The numbers 2 and 1 cannot be divided by the same number to give whole numbers, so this is the simplest form of the ratio.

Worked example

In a genetic cross, the predicted ratio of offspring is 3 long-haired : 1 short-haired. If there were 20 offspring, how many offspring would you expect to have long hair and how many would have short hair?

Step 1 Add the numbers in the ratio together: $3 + 1 = 4$

Step 2 Divide the total number of offspring by the number found in Step 1.

$20 \div 4 = 5$

This is how many each '1' in the ratio represents.

Step 3 Multiply each number in the ratio by the value found in Step 2.

Therefore, we expect there to be:

$3 \times 5 = 15$ long-haired offspring
$1 \times 5 = 5$ short-haired offspring

B Guided questions

1 **A genetic cross was carried out to determine the expected offspring from breeding two fish together. In this species of fish, red stripes are dominant to orange stripes. One of the fish was heterozygous and had red stripes, and the other was homozygous and had orange stripes.**

Use a Punnett square diagram to determine the expected ratio of offspring which have orange stripes to those which have red stripes.

Step 1 Use R for the dominant allele, and r for the recessive allele. The red-striped parent has a genotype of Rr. The orange striped parent has a genotype or rr.

Step 2 This gives the following genetic cross:

Parents: Rr   rr
Gametes: R   r   r   r

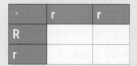

Step 3 Expected ratio of offspring = ...

C Practice question

2 An organism has an approximate volume of $8\,cm^3$ and an approximate surface area of $24\,cm^2$. What is the surface area : volume ratio of this organism?

Estimating results

When carrying out calculations, it can be useful to estimate the answer first. Estimates can mean that obvious mistakes are spotted. For example, if you enter the wrong number on your calculator, or divide instead of multiply while you are doing a calculation, an estimate shows you that your answer is clearly wrong. You can then re-check the calculation and correct your mistake.

Estimation is meant to be quick. This means you need to make the calculations as easy as possible. The best way to do this is to round each given value to the nearest ten, hundred or other convenient whole number. While your answer will not be the 'correct' number, it will be an approximate estimation of it.

★ **Not a specific requirement for WJEC Biology.**

Tip

While estimating is a useful skill that can help you check if a calculation is correct, in an exam it is important to use your calculator to find the value precisely and write this as the answer.

A Worked example

An area of the Amazon rainforest has suffered intense deforestation. The area affected was 33 km long by 1.89 km wide. Estimate the total area affected.

Step 1 For a quick estimation of the area, round both given values to make the calculation more straightforward.

> 33 km rounds down to 30 km
>
> 1.89 km rounds up to 2 km

Step 2 Perform the calculation with the rounded values.

This gives an estimated area of 30 km $\times$ 2 km = 60 km^2

When a calculator is used to find the area using the values stated in the question, it gives an answer of: 33 km $\times$ 1.89 km = 62.37 km^2

Clearly, the estimated and actual values are different: 60 km^2 is not the correct answer, but our estimate is close.

Tip

Estimates can also help you spot obvious mistakes in your answers. For example, in this question, if you had pressed ÷ instead of × on the calculator, we would have got 17.46 km^2, which looks wrong just from looking at it. We could then go back and correct the mistake.

B Guided questions

1 **The population of nematode worms in two samples of forest soil was investigated. Sample A had 781 651 worms while sample B contained 314 528. Estimate the total number of worms in the two samples.**

To estimate the total, round both numbers to the nearest 10 000 and then sum them.

Step 1 Round both numbers: .... + ...

Step 2 Sum of estimated total population = ...

2 **In an enzyme investigation, 12 g of product was produced in 19 mins. Estimate the rate of this reaction in g/min.**

Step 1 Round both 12 g and 19 mins to the nearest 10: .... and ....

Step 2 Find the rate of reaction by dividing mass of product over time.

Rate of reaction = ...

C Practice questions

3 In an investigation into diffusion, the time taken for equilibrium to be reached was recorded. The investigation was repeated three times.

196 minutes, 202 minutes, 190 minutes

Estimate the mean time taken to reach equilibrium in minutes.

4 During the day, a person's blood glucose concentration decreased from 6.3 mmol/L to 3.9 mmol/L. To estimate the percentage change in blood glucose concentration, a researcher did the following calculation:

$$\frac{3}{6} \times 100\% = 50\%$$

Is this the best estimate the researcher could have made? Explain your answer.

» Handling data

Using significant figures

Significant figures can be a complex topic, but there are some general rules for using them. There are exceptions to the rules outlined below, but these are unlikely to feature in a GCSE exam. In general, **all** digits are significant figures except in the instances below:

● Leading zeros are zeros before a non-zero digit. For example, 0.07 has two leading zeros, and these are not significant figures. 0.07 only has one significant figure (7). The zeros are written to make the place value correct.

● Zeros after a non-zero digit if they are due to rounding or used to indicate place value. For example, a value that is rounded to the nearest hundred (for example 600 g) has two trailing zeros which are not significant, and so it has only one significant figure (6). A value that is exactly 600 g, however, would have three significant figures, and the zeros in this case would be significant.

● Spurious digits are digits which make a calculated value appear more precise than the original data used in the calculation. For example, suppose that one side of a square was measured with a ruler to be 13.1 cm long. Using this measurement to calculate the area of the square gives a value of 171.61 cm² (13.1 × 13.1). The ruler measured only to three significant figures, while the answer appears to contain five significant figures. This means that the last two digits (6 and 1) are spurious and should not be included in the final answer. Therefore, the result should be rounded to 172 cm² (three significant figures as in the original measurement).

When two or more different pieces of measuring apparatus are used, calculated results should be reported to the limits of the least accurate measurement. This means that you should use the number of significant figures that the **least** accurate apparatus measures. This will usually mean using the same number of decimal places as the least accurate piece of apparatus. See pages 64–65 for more detail on precision, accuracy and resolution.

Tip
The term 'significant figures' can often be shortened to 's.f.' or 'sig fig'.

Key terms

Leading zero: A zero before a non-zero digit, for example 0.6 has one leading zero.

Place value: The value of a digit in a number, for example in 926, the digits have values of 900, 20 and 6 to give the number 926.

Trailing zeroes: Zeroes at the end of a number.

Spurious digits: Digits that make a calculated value appear more precise than the data used in the original calculation.

(A) Worked examples

1 **Identify how many significant figures the number 0.0304 has.**

Step 1 Identify the first non-zero digit from the left. This is 3.

Step 2 The two zeros to the left of 3 are leading zeros, and therefore not significant.

Step 3 The other four digits (3, 0 and 4) are significant.

Step 4 So this number has three significant figures.

2 **The mass of an adult human brain was recorded as 1368 g. Write this mass to two significant figures.**

Step 1 The first significant digit is 1, and the digit immediately to its right, 3, is the second significant digit. These are the two significant digits we need to use to work out our answer.

Step 2 To work out the answer, we need to determine if we can use 3 as the second significant figure (for example an answer of 1300) or will need to round it up to 4 (for example an answer of 1400). In order to work out if we should round up or down, look at the digit immediately to the right of 3.

Step 3 In this case the digit is 6, so we need to round 1368 up to 1400.

Step 4 Therefore, the mass is 1400 g to two significant figures. This could also be written as 1.4×10^3 g in standard form (see page 7 for more detail on standard form).

(B) Guided question

1 **Write the number 0.040891 to two significant figures.**

Step 1 Identify the first non-zero digit from the left (any leading zeros to its left are not significant): ....

Step 2 Identify the second significant figure that you need to keep: ....

Step 3 Look at the digit immediately to the right of the second significant figure and use it to decide whether to round up or down.

Answer to two significant figures: ....

(C) Practice questions

2 Write 5783 g to two significant figures.

3 Write 0.63830 mm to three significant figures.

4 During an investigation into the rate of an enzyme catalysed reaction, a balance was used to measure 71.6 g of product which was produced in 10.5 hours. This mass was used to calculate a rate of reaction of 6.819 g/hour. Write this answer to the correct number of significant figures.

Finding arithmetic means

The mean (often denoted by x̄ in tables or equations) is an 'average', and is calculated by adding all the individual values in a data set together and dividing by the total number of values used.

The mean is the most commonly used average in biology, and the one you will normally use in practical investigations. For example, you might use it when investigating the effect of light intensity on the number of bubbles produced by pond weed. Each light intensity can be repeated three times and a mean number of bubbles found.

Key term

Arithmetic mean: The sum of a set of values divided by the number of values in the set – it is sometimes called the average.

Using the mean when averaging data does have some disadvantages because it can be skewed by extreme (or outlier) results. An example of this is shown in the table below.

Table 1.3 Disadvantages of the mean

Temperature (°C)	20	20	20
Rate of reaction of protease (1 / time taken)	0.1	0.2	0.9

In this data set, 0.9 is very different from the other values so it seems highly likely that this value is an outlier. This means that it can be excluded when calculating the mean:

$$\frac{(0.1 + 0.2)}{2} = 0.15 \text{ (2 being the number of data values used to calculate the mean)}$$

If 0.9 had been included, this would give a mean value of:

$$\frac{(0.1 + 0.2 + 0.9)}{3} = 0.4$$

This second value is much larger than the mean calculated when not using the outlier, and so is not as representative of the data.

Tip

When outliers are present in a data set, it may be more appropriate to use another type of average (such as the median or mode — see page 23) or you can just discard the outlier values before calculating the mean.

A Worked examples

1   **The table below shows the results of a survey of a patient's white blood cell count over a week. Calculate their mean white blood cell count, giving your answer to the nearest whole number.**

Day	White blood cell count (cells / µl)
1	8000
2	8500
3	9000
4	8300
5	8600
6	8000
7	8100

Tip

Cells per microlitre (µl) is the unit used for white blood cell counts. You will not be expected to recall this unit.

Step 1 Add all the data values together:
8000 + 8500 + 9000 + 8300 + 8600 + 8000 + 8100 = 58 500

Step 2 Divide by the total number of data points, which is 7: 58 500 ÷ 7 = 8357.143

Step 3 As the question asks for the answer to the nearest whole number, round the answer down: 8357 cells/µl

2   **The table below shows the results of an investigation into the rate of reaction of amylase enzyme. Complete the two missing values in the table.**

Concentration of amylase / %	Time taken for solution to turn blue–black / seconds			
	1	2	3	Mean
20	300	350	376	342
40	270	278	266	
60	190	185	177	
80	124	131	121	125
100	45	62	58	55

Tip

In this table, all the mean values are given to whole numbers, so you should ensure that your answers are also given to whole numbers. This means that all the mean values will be consistent.

Step 1 Add the three time measurements together at 40% amylase concentration and divide by 3. This gives an answer of 271 seconds.

Step 2 Add the three time measurements together at 60% amylase concentration and divide by 3. This gives an answer of 184 seconds.

(B) Guided question

1   The data below shows the time taken for cells in a root tip to undergo meiosis. Calculate the mean time taken for the cells to undergo meiosis. Give your answer to two significant figures.

Cell	Time taken to undergo meiosis / hours
1	15
2	19
3	21
4	18
5	23

Step 1 Add all the times together: ....

Step 2 Divide the sum of the times by the number of data points:

.... ÷ .... = ...

> **Tip**
> • • • • • • • • • • •
> Although this question asks for an answer to two significant figures, you should not round the sum of the times taken to two significant figures. Instead, you should only round at the end of the calculation.

(C) Practice questions

2   The table below shows the results of an investigation into light intensity at three different sites. Complete the table to show the mean light intensity at site B.

Site	Light intensity (lumen)			
	1	2	3	Mean
A	1900	1800	1950	1883
B	1500	1600	1700	
C	1200	1350	1250	1267

3   The table below shows the results of an investigation into the time taken for amylase to break down starch.

Trial	Time taken for starch to be completely broken down (seconds)
1	350
2	400
3	90

Calculate the mean time taken for starch to be completely broken down. Explain how you arrived at your answer.

> **Tip**
> • • • • • • • • • • •
> Categorical data is an example of discontinuous data.
>
> The other type of data you will need to know about is continuous data.

Constructing frequency tables, bar charts and histograms

Data can be represented in a number of different ways. This section covers the use of frequency tables, bar charts and histograms.

Frequency tables and bar charts

Frequency tables show the frequency (how many times something occurs) within a data set. Frequency tables are particularly useful for giving an overview of data, or for calculating the mode (see page 23 for more detail on mode).

Bar charts can be used to show frequencies of categorical data (data which can be put into categories). The categories used are normally plotted on the x axis, while frequency is on the y axis. Unlike a histogram, the bars on a bar chart do not touch each other, this is to show that the bars represent distinct categories.

> **Key terms**
>
> Categorical data: Data that can take one of a limited number of values (or categories). Categorical data is a type of discontinuous data.
>
> Continuous data: Data that can have any value on a continuous scale, for example length in metres.
>
> Discontinuous data: Data that can have a limited range of different values, for example eye colour.

Worked example

The data below shows the results of an investigation into the ages at which a group of female elephants first became pregnant. All values are given in years.

18	22	24	22	19	18	20	20	20	20

Step 1 To construct the frequency diagram, write all of the ages in the left-hand column.

Step 2 Count the number of times each of the ages occur; this is their frequency. Record these numbers in the right-hand column.

Age at which females first became pregnant	Frequency
18	2
19	1
20	4
22	2
24	1

Plot the data in the frequency table as a bar chart.

For a bar chart, the horizontal axis would normally show the different categories of data (the ages in this case), and the vertical axis would show the values of the categories. The scale on the vertical axis should be linear (for example increase by the same value between successive graduations) and have an origin (a start point).

Step 3 Plot the data on the graph.

In a bar chart, for each category we draw a bar extending from the horizontal axis up to the value on the vertical axis associated with that category. The bars in a bar chart do not touch each other, indicating that the data is in separate, non-overlapping categories.

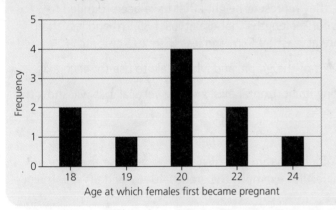

Tip

This data is categorical because each age is a distinct category and there is no overlap between the different categories. The best way to present such data is in a bar chart.

Tip

Scales can start at zero, but do not have to. See the chart in the worked example on page 18 for an example of this.

Tip

Frequency tables like this one are constructed in the same way as the frequency table in the worked example on page 18, except rather than grouping continuous data, it has definite categories.

 Guided question

1   The table below shows the results of a survey of bat species. Use the axis to draw a bar chart of this data.

Bat species	Frequency
Grey long-eared bat	2
Common pipistrelle	5
Noctule	1

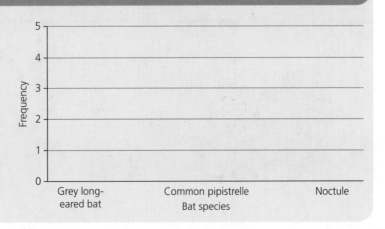

C Practice question

2 The table below shows the results of a wildflower survey. Draw a bar chart to show this data.

Wild flower species	Frequency
Cow parsley	16
Daisy	52
Cornflower	4
Cowslip	23

Histograms

Histograms are used to show the frequency in a continuous data set. They differ from bar charts in that they have a *continuous* scale on the *x* axis, and the bars touch.

A Worked example

The table below shows the results of a survey of giant redwoods. Plot this data on a histogram.

Height (m)	Frequency
20–39	5
40–59	4
60–79	7
80–99	8
100–119	1

Height is a continuous variable which can take any value in a continuous range. Although the numbers in the left-hand column of the table are whole numbers, they represent heights that have been rounded to the nearest metre. Therefore, the group 40–59 stands for 'all lengths that are at least 39.5 m and less than 59.5 m'; the group 60–79 stands for 'all lengths that are at least 59.5 cm and less than 79.5 cm', etc.

Step 1 Decide what information to show along each axis of the graph, and what scale to use for each axis.

The histogram will have the groups of tree heights along its horizontal axis, and the vertical axis will show the frequency of each of these groups.

Step 2 Plot the data on the graph.

A histogram looks similar to a bar chart, but the bars of a histogram touch each other because there are no 'gaps' between adjacent groups of continuous data values (for example, the groups 40–59 and 60–69 'touch' at 59.5).

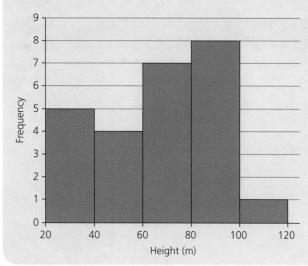

B Guided question

1 The data below shows the dry mass of a sample of GM crops.
   Draw a histogram of this data using the axes below.

Mass (g)	Frequency
0–49	1
50–99	6
100–149	15
150–199	3

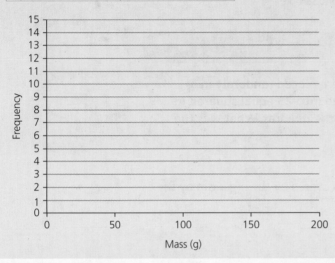

C Practice question

2 The table below shows the results of an investigation into resting heart
   rates. Draw a histogram of this data.

Resting heart rate (bpm)	Frequency
60–69	14
70–79	59
80–89	132
90–99	97

Understanding the principles of sampling

Sampling is a very wide-ranging practical topic. In this section, we will look at
the mathematics involved in some of the ecological sampling techniques that
may feature in GCSE Biology.

Quadrats

Quadrats are tools for assessing the abundance of non-mobile organisms such
as plants. Quadrats can be used to estimate:

● species frequency: the number of individuals of a certain species found in the
   sample area
● species density: the number of individuals of a certain species per unit area
● percentage cover: the percentage of the quadrat area that is occupied
   by individuals of a particular species. This measure is particularly useful
   for species where it would be difficult to count every individual plant, for
   example grasses.

Key terms

Ecological: The relation
of living organisms to
one another and to their
physical surroundings.

Quadrats: Tools for
assessing the abundance of
non-mobile organisms.

Mark and recapture

This sampling technique allows us to estimate the number of mobile organisms (for example woodlice) in a particular area.

First, a number of organisms of a certain species are caught from a defined area and marked. These organisms are then released. After a period of time, the same area is sampled again, and the marked individuals among this second sample are counted. The total population size can then be estimated using the equation:

$$\text{Population size} = \frac{(\text{total number in first sample} \times \text{total number in second sample})}{\text{number marked in second sample}}$$

A Worked examples

1   In a sampling activity, 0.25 m² quadrats were placed randomly in a 10 m by 10 m grid. Each quadrat was divided into 25 equal squares. In quadrat 1, grass filled 20 of the squares in the quadrat. What was the percentage cover of grass in this quadrat?

To find the percentage cover:

Step 1 Divide the area of the quadrat that is covered by the organism by the total area of the quadrat:

20 ÷ 25 = 0.80

Step 2 Multiply this answer by 100:

0.80 × 100 = 80%

So the percentage cover of grass in this quadrat is 80%.

2   During a sampling activity, 56 woodlice were caught, marked and then released. The sampling was then repeated a week later. In this second sampling, 60 woodlice were caught. 32 were found to be marked. Calculate the size of the woodlouse population.

Step 1 Use the capture-recapture equation to estimate the size of the woodlouse population.

Step 2 Substitute the given values into the capture-recapture equation:

Population size = (total number in first sample × total number in second sample) ÷ number marked in second sample

= (56 × 60) ÷ 32 = 3360 ÷ 32 = 105

Tip

In a capture-recapture exam question, you will be given the equation.

B Guided questions

1   During a survey of a crab population, 92 crabs were caught, tagged and then released. Several months later, 78 crabs were caught and of these, 15 had been tagged. Use the equation below to calculate the size of the crab population.

$$\text{Population size} = \frac{(\text{total number in first sample} \times \text{total number in second sample})}{\text{number marked in second sample}}$$

Step 1 Number in first sample = 92; number in second sample = 78; number marked in second sample = 15

Step 2 Population size = $\dfrac{(\text{...................} \times \text{...................})}{\text{number marked in second sample}}$ = $\dfrac{}{\text{.............................}}$

2 A survey of *Digitalis* was carried out in a field. The results of 10 quadrats are shown below. The area of each quadrat is 0.25 m².

Quadrat	1	2	3	4	5	6	7	8	9	10
Number of *Digitalis*	2	1	3	0	0	2	1	3	0	4

What was the species frequency of *Digitalis?*

Step 1 Count how many of the quadrats contained *Digitalis*. The number is: ....

Step 2 Divide the number of quadrats containing *Digitalis* by the total number of quadrats, and multiply by 100 to get a percentage:

Species frequency = (.................... ÷ ....) × 100 = ...%

C Practice questions

3 In an investigation into the population of snails in an area, 105 were caught and marked. Two weeks later, the sampling activity was repeated. Out of 120 snails caught, 45 were marked. Estimate the total size of the snail population.

4 During an investigation into a population of a species of grass, a quadrat with 25 equal squares was used to estimate the percentage cover. In one of the quadrats, 15 of the squares were covered with the grass. Estimate the percentage cover of the grass in this quadrat.

Simple probability

Probabilities are usually expressed as decimals or fractions, and sometimes as percentages. In GCSE Biology, you will encounter probability in the context of genetic crosses. If something is certain to happen, it has a probability of 1 (or 100%). If something is certain not to happen, it has a probability of 0.

The sum of the probabilities of all possible outcomes of an experiment is 1. Therefore, if the probability of an event occurring is 0.25, then the probability of that event not occurring is 0.75 (because 0.25 + 0.75 = 1).

A Worked examples

1 A species of snake can either have red or yellow markings. In a particular population of snakes, the probability of a snake having red markings is 0.65. What is the probability of a snake in this population having yellow markings?

Step 1 Determine all the possible outcomes – red or yellow. The probabilities of all possible outcomes add up to 1.

Step 2 Write an equation to show the probabilities of all possible outcomes adding up to 1.

Probability of red markings + probability of yellow markings = 1

Step 3 Rearrange this equation to make the probability of yellow markings the subject.

1 – probability of red markings = probability of yellow markings

Step 4 Solve this equation to find the probability of a snake having yellow markings.

1 – 0.65 = 0.35

The probability of a snake having yellow markings is 0.35.

2 In humans, the sex chromosomes (X and Y) determine biological sex. Males have XY and females have XX. Use a genetic cross to show the probability of a couple having a baby girl. Give your answer as a percentage.

Step 1 Write out the genotypes of the parents.

Parents:　　　　XX　　　　　XY

Step 2 Write out the gametes produced by the parents.

Gametes:　　X　　X　　X　　Y

Step 3 Use the gametes to draw a Punnett square to find the genotype of the offspring.

	X	Y
X	XX	XY
X	XX	XY

Step 4 Write out the expected offspring ratio.

Expected offspring ratio = 2 female (XX) : 2 male (XY) = 1 female : 1 male

Step 5 To calculate the probability of having a girl from this ratio, divide the number of females by the total of the numbers in the ratio. As the question asked for the answer as a percentage, you have to multiply your answer by 100

$\frac{1}{2} \times 100 = 50\%$

There is a 50% chance of the couple having a girl.

> **Tip**
>
> As probabilities are concerned with chance, there is always a possibility that the observed results do not match the expected results. This is the reason that, despite the most likely outcome of having two children being a boy and a girl, many parents actually have two girls or two boys.

B Guided question

1 Sarah and David have three boys. David thinks that it is more likely that they will have a girl next time rather than another boy. Is David correct? Explain your answer.

Step 1 Find the probability of having a boy.

Step 2 Is this probability greater than the probability of having a girl? If so, then David is correct; if not, then David is incorrect.

C Practice questions

2 In a species of plant, green fruit is the dominant phenotype and yellow fruit is the recessive phenotype. A genetic cross was carried out to estimate the results of crossing two heterozygous plants.

Draw a Punnett square diagram to determine the probability of the offspring having yellow fruit. Use the following symbols:

G = dominant allele

g = recessive allele

3 The probability of a guinea pig having long fur is 0.6. Two parent guinea pigs already have two offspring with short fur. What is the probability that their next offspring will have long fur?

Understanding mean, mode and median

The three types of average that you will come across in your GCSE Biology exam questions are:

1 Mean: this is the average, and is covered in the 'means' section on pages 14–15.

2 Median: this is the middle value in the data set. To find the median, arrange all the data points in order and pick out the middle value in the sequence. If there are an even number of data points, take the two in the middle and calculate their mean (add them together and divide by 2).

3 Mode: this is the most common value in the data set.

The most appropriate type of average to use depends on the context:

● The most commonly used average is the mean.
● The median is more useful than the mean if there are exceptionally high or low values (outliers) in the data, which would skew the mean.
● The mode is suitable for use with non-numerical data or when the data points cannot be put in a linear order.

★ **Understanding mode and median is not explicitly required by CCEA Biology.**

Tip
Even if a skill is not explicitly required by your exam board, you will likely cover it in Maths GCSE, so it can't hurt to refresh your memory.

A Worked examples

The following table shows the raw results of a survey of blood groups.

A	AB	AB	O	O	O
B	AB	A	A	B	AB

Find the mode of these blood groups.

Step 1 Draw a frequency table of each value.

Blood group	Frequency
A	3
B	2
O	3
AB	4

Step 2 Determine which is the most common blood group. AB has a frequency of 4, so the mode blood group is AB.

Tip
To avoid multiple entries, cross off data items (or highlight/circle them with a coloured pen) as you order the items for a median.

B Guided question

1 **Find the median of the following set of human BMIs.**

   19.6, 18.5, 21.5, 30.8, 28.1, 32.9, 23.2, 20.2, 22.4, 27.1

   Step 1 First, put the values in ascending order.

   18.5, 19.6, 20.2, 21.5, 22.4, 23.2, 27.1, 28.1, 30.8, 32.9

   Step 2 As there are an even number of values, find the mean of the middle two values: (..................... + ...) ÷ 2

   Median = ...

C Practice questions

2 The table below shows the estimated population sizes of a number of bacterial colonies. What is the median bacterial population size?

Sample	Estimated population size
1	4×10^5
2	6×10^3
3	3×10^8
4	5×10^4
5	2×10^5
6	9×10^7
7	1×10^9
8	1×10^6

3 The table below shows the results of an investigation into the symptoms shown by a group of diseased trees. What was the mode symptom?

Tree	Symptom
1	Spots on leaves
2	Areas of rot
3	Spots on leaves
4	Malformed stems
5	Stunted growth
6	Spots on leaves
7	Stunted growth

Using a scatter diagram to identify a correlation

When data points are plotted on a scatter diagram, it may be possible to identify correlations in the data. A correlation can be either positive or negative.

A positive correlation is one where as one variable increases, the other variable also tends to increase. A negative correlation means that as one variable increases, the other variable shows a decreasing trend.

★ Using a scatter diagram to identify a correlation between two variables is not explicitly required for CCES Biology GCSE.

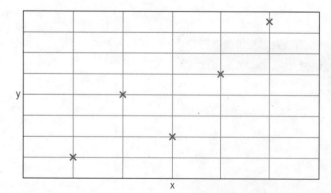

▲ Figure 1.1 Scatter diagram showing a positive correlation

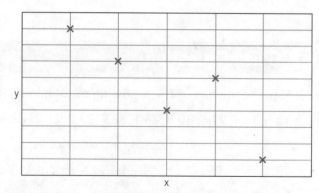

▲ Figure 1.2 Scatter diagram showing a negative correlation

In some situations it will be clear that correlation exists, but occasionally some data will show **no correlation**. If you are asked about scatter graphs in the exam, any correlation (positive, negative or none) should be evident.

A Worked examples

1 The scatter diagram below shows the effect of dissolved oxygen concentration on the population of rainbow trout in an aquaculture pond. What type of correlation is shown by this data?

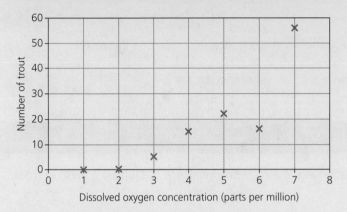

Step 1 Look for a general trend in the distribution of the points on the scatter diagram. As you move from left to right in the diagram, do the data points seem to be getting higher or lower?

Step 2 As the dissolved oxygen concentration increases, the population of the rainbow trout also increases. Not every data point fits the pattern exactly, but this should not be surprising, as data involving living organisms will always show variation.

Step 3 State the correlation shown. The scatter diagram indicates a positive correlation between the dissolved oxygen concentration and the population of rainbow trout.

2 The graph below shows the results of an investigation into effect of bacterial density on transmission of light through water.

What correlation is shown by this graph?

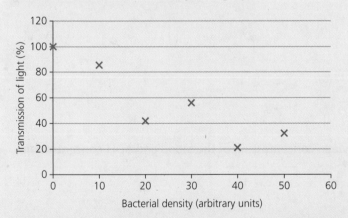

As the bacterial density increases, the transmission of light decreases. There is therefore a negative correlation between the bacterial density and transmission of light through the water.

Key terms

Scatter diagram: A graph plotted between two quantities to see if there might be a relationship between them.

Positive correlation: This occurs if one quantity tends to increase when the other quantity increases.

Negative correlation: This occurs if one quantity tends to decrease when the other quantity increases.

No correlation: There is no relationship whatever between two quantities.

Tip

Although a correlation between two variables may suggest a link between them, it does not prove that one factor causes the other. Correlation does not imply **causal relationship**.

Key term

Causal relationship: The reason why one quantity is increasing (or decreasing) is that the other quantity is also increasing (or decreasing).

B Guided question

1 The scatter graph below shows how the percentage cover of a grass species varies with distance from a large tree. What type of correlation is shown by this data?

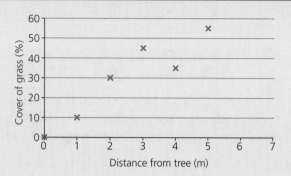

Step 1 Describe the correlation shown by the graph. As the distance from the tree increases, the percentage cover of grass increases.
Step 2 State the correlation shown. This shows a .... correlation.

C Practice questions

2 The graph below shows how nitrate concentration in soil affects the incidence of stunted growth in trees. What is the correlation shown by this graph?

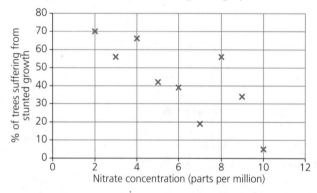

3 The graph below shows how gibberellin affects ripeness of fruit. What correlation is shown by this graph?

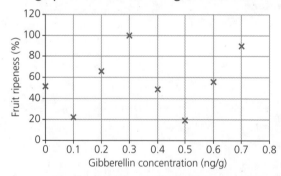

4 The graph below shows the relationship between concentration of the blood and ADH concentration. What is the correlation shown by this graph?

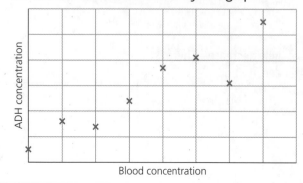

Making order of magnitude calculations

The two main uses of orders of magnitude in biology are interconverting units and the magnification equation.

Interconverting units

Prefixes are used to change the magnitude of a unit. The same prefixes are used for all units. The table below summarises how to apply prefixes correctly to units and interconvert between them.

Table 1.4 How to apply prefixes correctly to units and interconvert them

Prefix	Factor	Examples
kilo (k)	1×1000	kg, km, km²
deci (d)	$\dfrac{1}{10}$	dm³
centi (c)	$\dfrac{1}{100}$	cm, cm², cm³
milli (m)	$\dfrac{1}{1000}$	mm, mm², mm³, mg
micro (µ)	$\dfrac{1}{1000000}$	µm, µg
nano (n)	$\dfrac{1}{1000000000}$	nm, ng

For example, using the SI unit for length:

$0.001\,km = 1\,m = 100\,cm = 1000\,mm = 1000000\,µm = 1000000000\,nm$.

It is important that you select the appropriate unit for each situation, for example:

- It would be inappropriate to give the length of an organism in kilometres.
- Only the smallest organisms or structures would have their lengths measured in micrometres.

Using the magnification equation

Biology often involves studying organisms and structures that are incredibly small. The magnification equation makes it possible to determine the actual dimensions of these organisms and structures from micrographs and scale drawings. It also helps you to create your own scale drawings.

The magnification equation is:

Magnification = image size ÷ object size

You should be confident using and rearranging this equation to calculate:

- the magnification if you are given an image size and an object size
- the image size if you are given a magnification and an object size
- the object size if you are given a magnification and an image size.

An exam question on this skill might involve measuring part of a diagram or electron micrograph, so make sure you can do this accurately.

A Worked example

An electron micrograph of a nucleus showed it as having a diameter of 80 mm. The actual diameter of the nucleus was labelled as 0.0004 mm. What was the magnification of the electron micrograph?

Step 1 Identify the image size and the object size. The image size is the diameter of the electron micrograph. The object size is the actual diameter of the nucleus. Therefore:

Image size = 80 mm; object size = 0.0004 mm

Step 2 Substitute the values into the magnification equation: magnification = image size ÷ object size

Magnification = 80 ÷ 0.0004 = 200 000

Hence the magnification is 200 000.

> **Tip**
> Magnification is actually a ratio and therefore does not have a unit.

B Guided question

1   **A student used a microscope to make a drawing of a transverse section of a root. The diameter of the drawing was 150 mm. The student measured the width of the root using the microscope as 2 mm. Use the magnification equation to calculate the magnification of the student's drawing.**

Step 1 Identify the image size and the object size.

Step 2 Substitute the values into the magnification formula and calculate:

Magnification = image size ÷ object size

Magnification = ... ÷ .... = ...

C Practice question

2   On a diagram of a fungal cell, the cell had a width of 30 mm. The magnification was given as 340×. What was the actual width of the fungal cell? Give your answer in standard form to 2 significant figures.

» Algebra

Algebra is a branch of mathematics that uses equations in which letters represent numbers.

Biology students need to know how to solve various equations by:

- substituting in the correct numbers for each letter or value
- calculating the answer.

Understanding and using algebraic symbols

The following symbols are often used in algebra, and you may encounter them in GCSE Biology exam questions where equations are used. You should learn to recognise their meanings as below:

Table 1.5 Symbols in algebra

Symbol	Meaning
=	equals
>	**greater than**
≥	**greater than or equal to**
<	**less than**
≤	**less than or equal to**
∝	proportional to
~	approximately

★ **Knowledge of these symbols is not specifically required for WJEC or Edexcel International GCSE Biology.**

The bolded symbols are examples of inequalities because they show a relation between two values that are not equal.

A Worked examples

1 **The table below shows the rate of photosynthesis and rate of respiration in a plant at different times of the day.**

Time	Rate of respiration / arbitrary units	Rate of photosynthesis / arbitrary units
8 a.m.	40	70
12 p.m.	70	100
10 p.m.	50	0

Write inequalities that relate the rate of respiration to the rate of photosynthesis 12 p.m. and 10 p.m.

Step 1 Determine which of the rates is greater at 12 p.m. The rate of photosynthesis (100) is greater than the rate of respiration (70).
Step 2 Write the inequality for 12 p.m.: rate of photosynthesis > rate of respiration.
Step 3 Determine which of the rate is greater at 10 p.m. The rate of rate photosynthesis (0) is less than the rate of respiration (50).
Step 4 Write the inequality for 10 p.m.: rate of photosynthesis < rate of respiration.

2 **The below equation shows the relationship between distance from a light source and light intensity:**

$$\text{Light intensity} \propto \frac{1}{\text{distance}^2}$$

Write a sentence that summarises this relationship.
The symbol ∝ means 'proportional', so the relationship between distance from light source and light intensity can be summarised as:
Light intensity is proportional to one over the distance from the light source squared.

3 **During an enzyme investigation, 15.76 mg of product was produced. What whole milligram does this mass approximately equal?**

The mass 15.76 mg is approximately 16 mg, so 15.76 mg ~ 16 mg

B Guided question

1 **Within a certain range of temperatures, the rate of decomposition in soil is proportional to the soil temperature.**

Step 1 Write down the two factors with a space between them and consider which of the symbols best fits.

Rate of decomposition .... soil temperature

C Practice questions

2 Write an inequality that compares the blood pressure in arteries and veins.

3 Write an expression that links rate of reaction and enzyme concentration when substrate is not a limiting factor.

Substituting numerical values into equations and solving

This section involves substituting numbers for the letters or terms in an equation to calculate the value of an unknown quantity.

To solve an equation successfully, the key is to work carefully and logically through the steps, ensuring that all substitutions are done correctly and all the functions in the equation are evaluated accurately. It is particularly important to double-check all your working, as it is very easy to make mistakes in algebra.

There are no specific equations you need to learn for the biology exam, but you could be given a variety of different equations in the exam that you will have to substitute values into and calculate.

A Worked examples

1 **The rate of photosynthesis can be calculated using the following equation:**

Rate of photosynthesis = volume of oxygen produced ÷ time

If 5 cm³ of oxygen was produced in 9 minutes, what was the rate of photosynthesis in cm³/min? Give your answer to two decimal places.

Step 1 Substitute the values into the equation:

Rate of photosynthesis = volume of oxygen produced ÷ time
Rate of photosynthesis = $5 \div 9$

Step 2 Find the answer of this equation.

Rate of photosynthesis = 0.56 cm³/min

2 **The body mass index (BMI) equation is a method of determining if a person is overweight or underweight. The equation for BMI is:**

BMI = mass (kg) ÷ height (m)²

Calculate the BMI of a person who has a mass of 70 kg and a height of 1.6 m.

Step 1 Substitute the values into the equation: BMI = mass (kg) ÷ height (m)²

$$BMI = 70 \div 1.6^2$$
$$BMI = 70 \div 2.56$$
$$BMI = 27.3$$

> **Tip**
> Make sure you use any units that are given in a question in your answer.

> **Tip**
> BMI values do not have any units.

B Guided question

1 **Cardiac output can be calculated using the following equation:**

Cardiac output = stroke volume × heart rate

What is the cardiac output of a person who has a stroke volume of 55 cm³ and a heart rate of 65 beats per minute? Give your answer in cm³/min.

Step 1 Substitute the values into the equation:

Cardiac output = ... × ....

Step 2 Cardiac output = ...

C Practice question

2 **An investigation was carried out into effectiveness of different antibiotics, by comparing the areas of clear zones produced on bacterial cultures. The clear zones were approximately circular. The equation to calculate the area of the clear zones is shown below:**

Area of clear zone = πr^2

r = radius

The radius of one of the clear zones was 17 mm. Use the formula to calculate the area of this clear zone. Give your answer to the nearest whole number.

> **Tip**
> • • • • • • • • • • • • • •
> Exam questions involving pi will often give you a value to use in its place (for example pi (π) = 3.14). If it does not, you should use the pi button on your calculator. Make sure you round calculated answers appropriately.

Changing the subject of an equation

In addition to substituting values into an equation, you may also be required to change the subject of an equation. As in the previous section, you must ensure that you check your working carefully – it is very easy to make a mistake not only when substituting values but also when rearranging the terms in an equation.

★ **Changing the subject of the equation is only explicitly required for Edexcel International Biology GCSE.**

A Worked example

During a medical examination, a patient was determined to have a cardiac output of 4800 cm³/min. If the patient's heart rate was 60 beats per minute, what was their stroke volume? Use the equation below to calculate your answer.

Cardiac output = stroke volume × heart rate

Step 1 Rearrange the equation to make stroke volume the subject. Do this by dividing both sides of the equation by the heart rate. This gives:

Stroke volume = cardiac output ÷ heart rate

Step 2 Now substitute the values from the question into the equation.

Stroke volume = 4800 ÷ 60 = 80 cm³/min.

B Guided question

1   A ragworm has a diameter of 15 mm. A student draws a diagram where the ragworm is drawn with a magnification of 20 ×. What is the diameter of the ragworm in the drawing? Use the magnification equation below.

Magnification = image size ÷ object size

Step 1 As we want to find the diameter in the drawing, in other words the image size, we need to make it the subject of the equation. To do this, multiply both sides of the equation by the object size.

Magnification = image size = object size, which leads to
Image size = magnification × object size

Step 2 Substitute the given numbers into the equation and complete the calculation.

Image size = ... × .... = ...

C Practice questions

2   In a food chain, the energy available to the primary consumers can be calculated using the equation:

Energy available to primary consumers =
energy in primary producers − energy lost in respiration − energy lost by waste and death

If the energy available to primary consumers is 20 000 kJ, the energy lost in respiration is 30 000 kJ and the energy lost by waste and death is 150 000 kJ. What was the energy in the primary producers?

3   The population of a bacterial population can be estimated using the equation below:

Bacterial population = initial bacterial population × $2^{\text{number of divisions}}$

A nutrient broth was inoculated with a bacterial culture. The bacteria divided every three hours. After 15 hours, there were 3200 bacteria in the nutrient broth. How many bacteria were in the original culture?

❯❯ Graphs

An important maths skill in biology is translating information between graphical and numerical form. This can take a number of different forms, including reading values off a graph or finding gradients and intercepts.

> **Tip**
> You can use a ruler to read points off a graph. This can help ensure that you do not make mistakes.

Understanding that $y = mx + c$ represents a linear relationship

The graph of a linear relationship plotted on x and y axes is a straight line, and can be represented by the equation $y = mx + c$ where:

> ★ **Not explicitly required for WJEC, CCEA or Edexcel International Biology GCSE.**

- m = gradient of the line
- c = y intercept (the point where the line crosses the y axis).

Therefore, if the line has a gradient of 2 and the y intercept is 0.1, the equation of the line would be: $y = 2x + 0.1$

This means that if $x = 4$ then y would be:

$y = 2 \times 4 + 0.1 = 8.1$

In GCSE Biology exams, you could be asked to sketch a graph of a linear relationship. As the graph is a straight line, only two points are needed to draw the line, although it is recommended that you use a third point to check whether the line is correct.

If a set of axes is given in the question, it does not particularly matter which values on the *x* axis you use to construct the line, as long as their corresponding *y* values are within the range shown on the *y* axis. However, using points fairly far apart could make the line easier to draw accurately.

If the question leaves it up to you to draw the axes, make sure that the scale you choose for each axis covers the range of values in the given data. Do this by finding the maximum and minimum *y* values before starting to draw the axes.

Tip

When drawing graphs, always:
- draw it in pencil and draw the axes with a ruler (and have an eraser handy)
- use graph paper for accuracy (otherwise your graph is just a sketch)
- label your axes, giving units where appropriate
- draw a line graph unless told otherwise.

(A) Worked examples

1 **On the axes below, sketch a graph of the equation $y = 3x$.**

Step 1 Identify the values of *m* and *c* in the linear equation.

This is an equation of the form $y = mx + c$ with $m = 3$ and $c = 0$.

Therefore, the graph is a straight line with a gradient of 3 and a *y* intercept at 0.

Step 2 To construct the graph, choose two *x* values (within the range shown on the given *x* axis) and calculate their corresponding *y* values using the equation.

Using the points $x = 1$ and $x = 5$:

At $x = 1$, $y = 3 \times 1 + 0 = 3$

At $x = 5$, $y = 3 \times 5 + 0 = 15$

Step 3 Plot these points on the set of axes and draw a straight line through them.

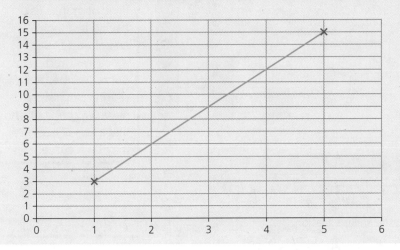

2 **The effect of enzyme concentration on the rate of a reaction can be predicted by the equation $y = 2x + 4$. Sketch the graph of this relationship on the axes provided.**

Step 1 Identify the values of m and c in the linear equation. The given equation is of the form $y = mx + c$ with $m = 2$ and $c = 4$.

Step 2 Choose two x values (within the range shown on the given x axis) and calculate their corresponding y values:

At $x = 1, y = 2 \times 1 + 4 = 6$

At $x = 5, y = 2 \times 5 + 4 = 14$

Step 3 Plot these points on the set of axes and draw a straight line through them.

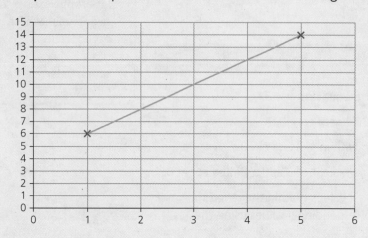

B Guided question

1 **Sketch the graph of $y = -0.5x + 9$.**

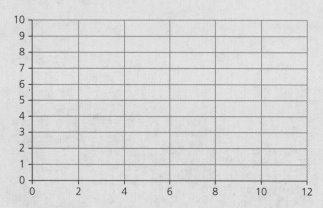

Step 1 Identify the values of m and c in the linear equation.

In this equation, $m =$ .... and $c =$ ....

Step 2 Choose two x values (within the range shown on the given x axis) and calculate their corresponding y values.

At $x = 0, y =$ ....

At $x = 10, y =$ ....

Step 3 Plot these points on the your of axes and draw a straight line through them.

Tip

Students often think of graphs as having a straight line of best fit and a positive gradient, but remember that graphs can have a negative gradient, and that a line of best fit may be a curve.

Tip

As the gradient (m) is negative, the graph is a straight line with negative gradient so slopes downwards from left to right.

C Practice question

2 Sketch the graph of $y = 3x + 4$.

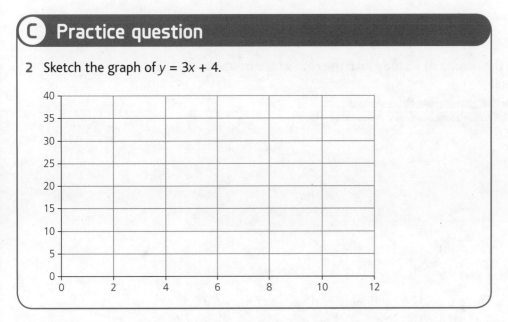

Plotting two variables from experimental or other data

This section will cover how to plot line graphs of experimental data. For information on plotting bar charts and histograms, see pages 16–18.

When plotting line graphs, take your data – which may exist in a different format (such as a table) – and plot the independent variable on the horizontal axis and the dependent variable on the vertical axis. While drawing the axes this way round is not essential, it is the way that it is normally done in science, as it allows you to see clearly the relationship between the independent and the dependent variable.

Ensure that each axis has a continuous scale and an origin. The origin should be appropriate for a graph, but does not have to be zero or be the same for both axes. For example, if a data set used to draw a graph runs from 100–200 then it would be logical not to have zero as an origin; 90 or 100 could be used instead.

> **Key terms**
>
> Continuous scale: A scale that has equal spaced increments.
>
> Origin: The start of an axis of a graph.

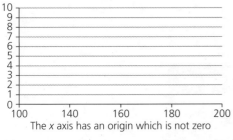

The x axis has an origin which is not zero

▲ **Figure 1.3** Non-zero origin graph

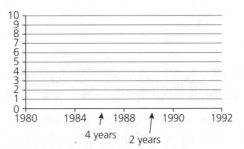

4 years   2 years

The x axis is not a continuous scale because it does not go up in equal increments. This would be incorrect.

▲ **Figure 1.4** Non-continuous scale graph

> **Tip**
>
> A common mistake in answering these types of questions is to have a scale on the horizontal axis that is not linear (for example does not increase by the same value from each marked number to the next).

Once you have your axes and scale, use the graph grid to help you mark with a cross (×) the position of each data point by reading up from the horizontal axes and across from the vertical axes to see where the two meet.

A Worked example

The table below shows the results of a study into the rate of transpiration over a period of 24 hours.

Time (hours)	Rate of transpiration (arbitrary units)
0	1
4	4
8	10
12	15
16	8
20	3
24	2

Plot the data on a graph.

Step 1 Draw suitable axes. These should be continuous and have an origin. A zero origin for both axes can be used in this case.

Step 2 Label the axes with the correct headings. Use the headings from the table as your axis titles.

Step 3 Plot the points carefully, and double check each of your plots.

Step 4 Join the points with a ruler or draw a curved line of best fit.

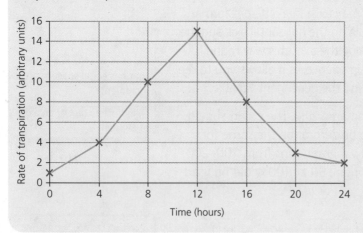

Tip

Some exam boards prefer you to draw curved lines of best fit, whereas others prefer the points to be joined with straight lines. Check with your teacher what you should do in exam questions.

B Guided question

1   The table below shows the results of an investigation into the effect of temperature on the rate of decomposition in soil..

Temperature (°C)	Rate of decomposition (arbitrary units)
10	2
20	15
30	42
40	92
50	21
60	6

Plot this data on a graph.

The *x* axis needs to run from 10 to 60, and the *y* axis from 2 to 92. The axes below would be suitable to plot the graph.

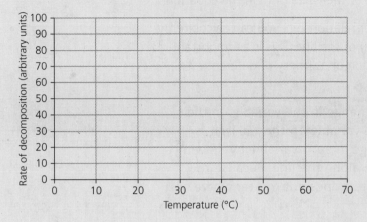

C Practice question

2 The table below shows the results of a survey of MRSA cases in an area over a period of time.

Time (months)	Number of MRSA cases
0	50
1	200
2	140
3	195
4	130

Plot the data on a graph.

Determining the slope and intercept of a linear graph

Determining intercept

In biological investigations, you may need to find an intercept of a graph, for example the point where the graph crosses one of the axes. This skill is most often applied in problems involving osmosis. In this example, the intercept is used to estimate the point where there is no change in mass when plant tissue is placed in a variety of different solvent concentrations.

In exam questions, you would normally be asked to find the intercept on the *x* axis. To do this, either read off the *x* value at which the line or curve crosses the *x* axis or, if the crossing point is not shown on the graph, you may be able to extrapolate from the line to where it would intersect the axis.

> **Key terms**
>
> Intercept: The point on a graph where the line crosses one of the axes.
>
> Extrapolate: Extending a graph to estimate values.

Determining slope

We have seen that a linear relationship can be represented by a straight line on a graph, or by the equation $y = mx + c$. The rate of change of the linear relationship is the gradient of the line graph, or the value of m in the equation.

When provided with a graph showing a linear relationship, you can calculate the rate of change by finding the slope (gradient) of the line. This is an important skill in biology because it allows the calculation of a variety of different rates, including rates of reaction.

To find the gradient of a line, divide the change in the variable on the y axis by the corresponding change in the variable on the x axis. It is easiest to determine the amount of change in each variable by drawing a right-angled triangle with its hypotenuse along the line. Because the gradient is the same at all points on a line, it does not matter where on the line you place this triangle.

Key term

Hypotenuse: The longest side of a right-angled triangle.

(A) Worked examples

1 **The graph below shows the change in mass of a potato sample placed in different concentrations of glucose solution. At what concentration of glucose would there be no change in mass?**

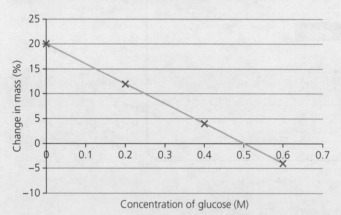

Tip

When there is 0% change in mass, the concentration inside the cells of the tissue equals the concentration of the solution that the tissue has been placed in.

We need to find the value of x (concentration of glucose) at which the y value (change in mass) is zero; this is the x axis intercept.

In this case, the intercept is straightforward to work out:

Step 1 Simply draw a straight line through the data points and look for where it crosses the x axis.

Step 2 Read off the x value where the line crosses the x axis. In this example, 0.5 M glucose solution gives a 0% change in mass.

2   **The graph below shows the volume of methane in a biogas generator over time. What is the rate of change of methane volume? Give your answer in m³/hour.**

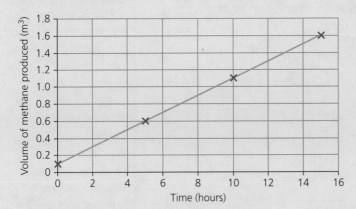

The rate of change is the gradient of the line.

Step 1 To find the gradient, draw a right-angled triangle as shown below. The triangle has a vertical edge and a horizontal edge, and its hypotenuse (slanted edge) lies along the line graph.

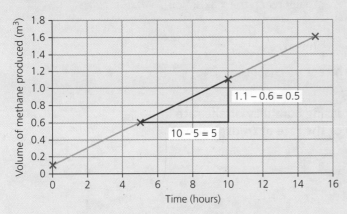

Step 2 Use the triangle to determine the change in x and the change in y : ....

Change in y = length of vertical edge of triangle
Change in x = length of horizontal edge of triangle

Step 3 Substitute these values into the equation below:

Gradient = change in y ÷ change in x
= $(1.1 - 0.6) \div (10 - 5) = 0.5 \div 5$
= 0.1 m³/hour

B Guided questions

1 **The graph below shows the change in mass of pumpkin tissue placed in different concentrations of sodium chloride. Predict at what concentration there will be no change in mass.**

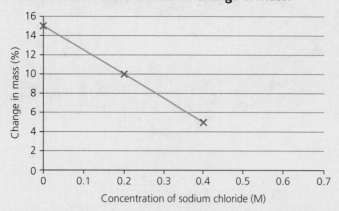

Tip

As this question involves extrapolating, it reduces our confidence in the accuracy of our answer. A follow-up investigation could be carried out with concentrations of sodium chloride around the predicted intercept, to see if the extrapolation was correct.

Step 1 As change in mass is shown on the y axis, no change in mass means $y = 0$, therefore you are looking for the line's intercept with the x axis.

Step 2 Because the line in the graph does not actually reach the x axis, you need to extend it to the x axis.

Step 3 Then read off the x value where it meets the axis.

Concentration of sodium chloride at which there is no change in concentration = ...

2 **The graph below shows the effect of increasing humidity on the rate of transpiration. What is the rate of change of the rate of transpiration?**

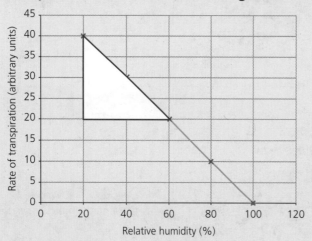

The rate of change is the gradient of the line.

Step 1 To find the gradient of the line, first draw a right-angled triangle with the hypotenuse on the line.

Step 2 Next, read off the change in y by looking at the vertical edge of the triangle, and the change in x by looking at the horizontal edge of the triangle.

Change in x = ...

Change in y = ...

Step 3 Finally, substitute the two numbers into the formula:

Gradient = change in y ÷ change in x

Gradient = ... ÷ ....

Step 4 Rate of change of rate of transpiration = ...

C Practice questions

3 The graph below shows the results of an investigation into osmosis in a sample of onion tissue. What was the internal concentration of the onion cells?

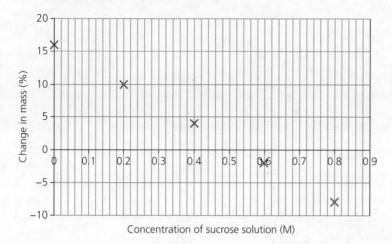

Concentration of sucrose solution (M)

4 The graph below shows the results of an investigation into the breakdown of starch by amylase. What is the fastest rate of reaction achieved during this investigation? Explain how you arrived at your answer.

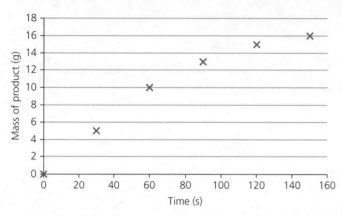

Time (s)

»» Geometry and trigonometry

Geometry deals with shapes and size. Trigonometry deals with the lengths and angles in triangles. Biological organisms and structures are often represented as simple shapes such as cubes or rectangles, and sampling activities often require the calculation of areas or angles.

Calculating areas, surface areas and volumes of cubes

Biological organisms and structures are often represented as simple shapes such as cubes. Therefore, you may be asked to calculate various areas and volumes.

Areas of triangles and rectangles

The area of a triangle can be calculated using the formula:

Area of triangle = (height × base) ÷ 2

The area of a rectangle can be calculated using the formula:

Area of rectangle = length × width

Key terms

Geometry: The branch of mathematics concerned with shapes and size.

Trigonometry: The branch of mathematics concerned with the lengths and angles in triangles.

Tip

Alternatively, if you find it easier, you can use the formula:

Area of triangle = 0.5 × (height × base)

This is because dividing by 2 is equivalent to multiplying by $\frac{1}{2}$ or 0.5

A Worked examples

1 **The diagram below shows the dimensions of an area used in a sampling activity. Calculate the sample area.**

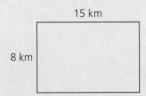

15 km

8 km

Step 1 The sample area is a rectangle. The formula for the area of a rectangle is:

   Area of rectangle = length × width

Step 2 The dimensions of the sample area are: length = 15 km; width = 8 km

Step 3 Substitute these values into the equation:

   Area of sample area = 15 km × 8 km = 120 km²

2 **A leaf is roughly a triangle shape, with a height of 6 cm and a base of 3 cm. Calculate the area of the leaf.**

Step 1 The formula for the area of a triangle is:

Area of triangle = (height × base) ÷ 2

Step 2 The dimensions of this triangle are: height = 6 cm; base = 3 cm

Step 3 Substitute these values into the equation:

   Area of triangle = (6 × 3) ÷ 2 = 9

   Area of leaf = 9 cm²

Surface areas and volumes of cubes

The surface area of one side of a cube (a square) can be calculated using the formula:

   Area of square = length × width

As there are six sides to a cube, the total surface area of a cube is:

   Surface area of a cube = length of one side × width of one side × 6

The formula for the volume of a cube is:

   Volume of a cube = length × width × height

As all the sides of a cube are the same length, this formula can be simplified to:

   Volume of a cube = length of one side³

Exam questions covering this skill may involve calculation of ratios, such as surface area to volume ratios. See the 'Fractions, percentages and ratios' section on pages 9–11 for more information on using ratios.

A Worked example

A cube of soil has a side length of 4 cm. Find the surface area and volume of this cube.

Step 1 The formula for the volume of a cube is:

Volume of a cube = length × width × height

As all sides of a cube are the same length, the length, width and height of a particular cube are all the same value. This means that the question only needs to give you the dimension of one side and you will know the length of all the sides.

Step 2 The volume of this cube is: 4 cm × 4 cm × 4 cm = 64 cm³

Step 3 The formula for the surface area of a cube is:

Surface area of cube = area of one face × number of faces
= side length × side length × number of faces

A cube always has six sides, so the number of sides will always be six.

Step 4 The surface area of this cube is 4 cm × 4 cm × 6 = 96 cm².

> **Tip**
> • • • • • • • • • • • •
> The units for volume will be distance cubed (for example, in this case cm³) while the units for surface area are cm².

B Guided questions

1 **Calculate the surface area : volume ratio of a cube which has a side length of 5 mm.**

   Step 1 First calculate the surface area of the cube:

   Surface area of cube = side length × side length × number of faces
   Surface area of cube = ... × .... × 6
   Surface area = ... mm²

   Step 2 Now calculate the volume of the cube:

   Volume of cube = length × width × height
   Volume of cube = ... × .... × ....
   Volume = ... mm³

   Step 3 Finally, put these two values into a ratio.

   Surface area : volume = ... : ....

2 **As part of a microbiology investigation, an agar plate was divided into eight triangles. Each triangle had a base of 50 mm and a height of 38 mm. What is the area of one of these triangles?**

   Area of triangle = (height × base) ÷ 2

   Step 1 area of triangle = (..................... × ....) ÷ 2

   Step 2 area of triangle = ... ÷ 2

   Area of triangle = ... mm²

C Practice questions

3 A rectangular area of grassland was destroyed in a fire. The length of the affected area is 700 m and the width is 400 m. What is the total area of the affected grassland?

4 As part of an investigation into homeostasis, a triangular section of kidney was extracted from a dead mammal and placed on a microscope slide. The section had a length of 17 mm and a width of 0.9 mm. What was the area of the section of the kidney?

5 In an investigation into diffusion, two different gelatine cubes were used. One had a side length of 6 cm and the other had a side length of 4 cm. Which of the cubes has the largest surface area to volume ratio? Show how you arrived at your answer.

Using angular measures in degrees

An angle is the space between two intersecting lines or surfaces. Angles are often measured in degrees (°). Some common angles are:

- 360° is a full circle
- 180° is a half turn
- 90° is a right angle.

This information can be used to determine unknown angles. For example, if you know that one of the two angles which makes up a half turn is 90° then the other must be 90° because 90° + 90° = 180°.

This skill could be used to determine angles in a subdivided petri dish, or the angle that light strikes an object.

★ **Only explicitly required for CCEA Biology GCSE students.**

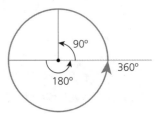

▲ Figure 1.5 Angle diagram

A Worked example

The diagram below shows a ray of light hitting a leaf. If angle $a = b$, what is angle a?

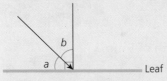

Step 1 As $a + b$ = a right angle, this means that: $a + b = 90°$

Step 2 As $a = b$, this means: $2a = 90°$

Step 3 Rearrange this to make a the subject: $a = 90 \div 2 = 45°$

Tip

As this example shows working out unknown angles is basically just using simple equations:
- Sum of angles on a whole turn = 360°
- Sum of angles on a half turn = 180°
- Sum of angles in a right angle = 90°

B Guided question

1 During a microbiological investigation, a circular petri dish was divided into six equal sections, as shown in the diagram below.

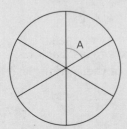

What is angle A? Show how you arrived at your answer.

Step 1 As the petri dish is a circle, the sum of all the angles is 360°.

Step 2 As the dish has been divided into six equal sections, to calculate A you need to divide 360° by 6.

A = 360 ÷ 6

A = ...

C Practice question

2 A circular section of plant tissue was used in a study. A 120° section of the tissue was removed for analysis. What proportion of the tissue had been removed? Show how you arrived at your answer.

2 Literacy

The biology exam papers will include extended response questions. In these questions, you will be tested on your ability to construct and develop a sustained line of reasoning. These answers need to be:

- coherent – the points made in the answer are clear
- relevant – the points made in the answer all answer the question
- substantiated (for example backed up) – the points made in the answer are supported by scientific knowledge
- logically structured – the answer is well laid out, with points arranged in a logical order.

Extended response questions will usually be worth 6 marks, and must be written in extended prose. This section will take you through the key points of answering these questions. The examples in this section all feature extended prose.

≫ How to write extended responses

The first step in answering extended response questions well is to learn how to recognise them:

- Extended response questions will often use command words such as 'Evaluate', 'Explain', 'Design' and 'Compare'.
- These questions may require you to link knowledge, understanding and skills from more than one area of the specification, for example linking work on osmosis to the action of the hormone ADH.
- Extended response questions can also be multi-step calculations, although this is less likely in the biology exam than in the chemistry or physics papers.

> **Tip**
> Look at recent papers for your examination board to ensure that you can recognise the extended response questions.

The most important part of an extended response question is identifying the command word – the key word that tells you what to do. Make sure your answer relates back to this command word, and answers the question asked.

Along with command words, extended response questions will often contain data and other key information. It is very important that you reference this data or information in your answer if provided – it is there for a reason. You may also occasionally see 'advice' in the question of what you need to cover to get top marks. Again, if this is the case, make sure you use it.

An example of how to identify an extended response is given on the following page.

A Worked example

The table below shows the results of an investigation into the effect of temperature on the action of lipase.

Temperature (°C)	pH of solution
20	7
40	2
60	5
80	7

Explain the results of this investigation. [6]

In this question, you can see that the command word is 'Explain'. It is a good idea to underline or highlight key terms and information in the question, and particularly the command word(s). This will help you to focus on the important aspects of the question.

The important data and information are clearly presented in this question as part of a table, but sometimes they will be in the text of the question.

There is no extra advice to help in this question, so it should be quite straightforward. Your answer does not require large amounts of information about the action of lipase in the body, and should focus on why the pH is changing due to the production of fatty acids and the effect of temperature on the lipase.

How to plan your answer

When planning your answer, the first thing to do is to read the question carefully. This means reading it at least twice and underlining the key points. A failure to properly understand the question will mean that you could end up writing completely the wrong thing and dropping marks.

Writing a plan will help you shape your answer, to ensure you cover everything in a logical fashion and maximise your chances of getting full marks. A plan should only take a small amount of extra time, but it is important. It could be a brief bullet-pointed list, a table or a simple mind map.

Looking at the question before, you already know that you must use the data in the question in your answer, and you need to explain why the results show the trend they do, rather than just describing the data. As mentioned previously, this question does not require large amounts of information about the action of lipase in the body, and therefore the answer should focus on why the pH is changing due to the production of fatty acids and the effect of temperature on the lipase.

Example of a bullet-pointed list plan:

- Lipase produces <u>fatty acids</u> – more fatty acids produced in 5 mins – faster rate of reaction – low pH.
- <u>Rate of reaction</u> varies with temperature.
- Low temperature – less <u>kinetic energy</u>.
- As temperature increases – more successful collisions.
- High temperature – <u>denatures enzyme</u>.

This is a clear plan in note form which could be written quickly. It covers all of the key points that are needed to answer this question fully.

The points are arranged in a logical order, therefore can be followed when writing out the answer, and checked off as they are written. You could also write numbers by the bullet points if you decided another order would be more logical. Key terms are also underlined, to make it easier to ensure they are included.

You will probably need to spend more time on a six-mark extended response question than you would on three separate two-mark questions. A rushed extended response question is unlikely to score in the highest band. For this reason, you need to be aware of how much time to spend on these types of questions, especially as you need a minute or so to write a rough plan. More advice on timings in an exam can be found on pages 83–84.

How to check your answer

Once you have written your answer, it is a good idea to check that you have not made any careless mistakes. Read back over your answer carefully and ask yourself:

- Have I covered everything in my answer, including any relevant examples or information given in the question?
- Is it coherent and logical?
- Is all the material relevant?
- Are there any spelling, punctuation or grammatical mistakes?

Correct spelling of key scientific words is important, but you should aim to spell all words correctly. It is a good idea to learn the spelling of the ones given in the table below, which are often commonly misspelt.

Table 2.1 Correct spellings

Mitosis	Vaccination	Gibberellins
Meiosis	Chlorosis	Recessive
Diffusion	Aerobic	Speciation
Osmosis	Anaerobic	Archaea
Capillaries	Ciliary muscles	Protist
Communicable	Pituitary	Dialysis

How to do well in extended response questions

The biggest difference between extended response questions and other question types is that these questions are marked using 'banded' mark schemes.

In extended response questions, you will be awarded marks according to the level of skill and knowledge that you show in your answer. This level is determined by:

- the overall quality of the answer
- the indicative content for each level.

Your answer will then be placed into the level that it best fits in to. Once the level has been determined, the actual mark you receive within that level depends on the quality of your response.

> **Tip**
>
> Do not just write everything you know about a topic. This can be very tempting, and is therefore a common mistake. However, including points that are not relevant will not only reduce your marks, but it could also waste time. That is why planning is a good idea – it will help you to identify the relevant points and frame the answer logically.

A general example of a six-mark extended response mark scheme is shown below:

Table 2.2 Example of a six-mark extended response mark scheme

Level	Description	Mark
Level 3	A clear, logical and coherent answer containing only relevant material.	5–6
Level 2	A partial answer with errors and some relevant material.	3–4
Level 1	One or two relevant points but lacks logical reasoning and contains errors.	1–2
	No relevant content.	0

Mark schemes will also include a list of 'indicative content.' These will be key points that are relevant to the question. You do not have to cover all these points to score full marks, just most of them. They are a useful revision tool when practising extended response questions.

Using the mark scheme above as an example:

- If a student's answer met all of the criteria for level 2 but not all of those for level 3, it would be placed in level 2. This could be due to the student including non-relevant information.
- If the student had written a good answer that only just missed out on level 3, they would be awarded 4 marks – the top of level 2.
- If, on the other hand, they had only achieved the very minimum to get into level 2, then they would be awarded 3 marks.

>> How to answer different command words

Work through the following extended writing questions, which look at the main extended response command words. This will help you to further understand how to write a good, longer-form answer.

For each command word there is:

- an 'expert commentary' question which gives a sample student response, along with an analysis of what is good and bad about it
- a 'peer assessment' question where you will be given the chance to apply what you have learnt to mark a sample answer yourself
- an 'improve the answer' question where you will be asked to improve another student's response in an attempt to get full marks.

Extended responses: Describe

In a 'Describe' question, your answer should give an account of what happens in a particular process. You should ensure that your answer is detailed, and uses as many keywords as possible.

Tip

The key to answering extended response questions is to ensure that your answer contains all the elements that will ensure it is placed in the top band.

Tip

When revising, try to write an extended response answer that covers every one of these 'indicative content' points.

(A) Expert commentary

1   **Describe how the bacteria MRSA evolved to be antibiotic resistant, and how doctors, patients and farmers can all work to reduce the chance of future development of antibiotic-resistant bacteria.** **[6]**

Student answer

Antibiotics have been widely used for many years. MRSA bacteria which mutate to become antibiotic-resistant have an advantage over those bacteria which do not have this mutation.

This means that they are more likely to survive and pass on the genes for antibiotic resistance. This process repeats and means antibiotic-resistant MRSA has become more prevalent. It is very important that doctors, farmers and patients all work to reduce antibiotic resistance.

This is a level 2 answer which would probably score four marks.

The first part of this answer is a good, detailed description of the evolution of antibiotic-resistant bacteria.

Tip

See pages 107–110 to find model answers to all expert commentary questions.

While the first part of the answer is very good, the student clearly did not know how to answer the final part of the question about how different groups can work to reduce antibiotic resistance. The student just restates what is in the question, and makes no attempt to describe how these groups can reduce antibiotic resistance.

(B) Peer assessment

2   **Describe the process of in vitro fertilisation (IVF) treatment.** **[6]**

Student answer

Eggs are collected from the mother. They are then mixed with some sperm from the father in the lab, and fertilisation takes place. These fertilised eggs develop into embryos, which are then grown in test tubes. At the start, the mother is given FSH, which are an enzyme, which stimulates the maturation of several eggs.

Use the mark scheme and indicative content below to award this answer a level and a mark.

Mark scheme

Level	Description	Mark
Level 3	A clear, well-structured and logical answer where all the material is relevant. The answer clearly sets out the process of IVF, including the use of FSH and LH, extraction of eggs, creation of embryos and implantation of the embryos into the mother.	5–6
Level 2	A reasonably clear and logical answer with some structure, where most of the material is relevant. Some parts of the process are not fully detailed.	3–4
Level 1	Few relevant points, a lack of clear structure or logical reasoning. The student gives a limited description of IVF which contains errors.	1–2
Level 0	No relevant content.	0

Indicative content:
- The mother is given FSH and LH to stimulate the maturation of several eggs.
- The eggs are collected from the mother.
- The eggs are fertilised in the laboratory by sperm taken from the father.
- The fertilised eggs develop into embryos.
- Once the embryos are a small ball of cells, one or two are inserted into the mother's uterus.

I would give this a level of .... and a mark of ....

This is because ...

....

....

....

C Improve the answer

3 Describe how the water level of the body is controlled by negative feedback. [6]

Student answer

The water level in the body is controlled by the antibody AHD. AHD is released when the concentration of the blood is too high. The AHD acts on the kidney tubules, and causes less water to be reabsorbed into the blood and more water to be released in the urine. AHD is released by the pituitary gland. This is an example of negative feedback.

Re-write this answer to improve it and obtain the full six marks.

Extended responses: Explain

In an 'Explain' question, you should be stating *why* something is happening. Your answer should apply your scientific knowledge to the example given in the question, and explain the process fully, in as much detail as possible.

Tip

Students often get confused between 'Describe' and 'Explain' questions. In 'Explain' questions, you are asked to say *why* something is happening, while 'Describe' questions are just saying *what* is happening.

A Expert commentary

1 The image below shows a potometer. Explain how this apparatus could be used to determine the effect of wind speed on the rate of transpiration. In your answer, make reference to how you would ensure that the results gained are repeatable. [6]

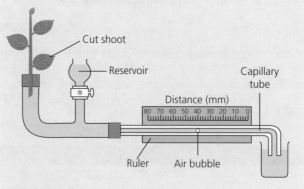

The student states correctly that a potometer measures the rate of uptake of water, but does not relate this to transpiration.

The student is correct to say that a fan can be used to change the wind speed. However, just using and then not using a fan is not a detailed enough explanation of how the independent variable (wind speed) can be changed.

The student is correct to talk about repeating the investigation and using these repeats to calculate a mean. They have also related this point back to repeatability, which is mentioned specifically in the question.

Student answer

The potometer measures the rate of uptake of water by the plant. Water travels up the xylem in the stem, into the leaves and then exits the leaves through the stomata. To show the effect of wind speed, you should get a fan, and measure the rate of transpiration without using the fan and then with the fan blowing. You can measure the rate of transpiration by seeing how far the bubbles move in a certain time. In order to ensure the results are repeatable, repeat the investigation three times at each wind speed, and calculate a mean rate of transpiration. Also ensure that all other variables (temperature, light intensity, etc.) are kept constant throughout the investigation.

This is a level 3 answer which would probably score five marks.

The section on the movement of water is correct, but it is not really relevant to the question. This could be an example of the student answering the question they wish was being asked, as opposed to the one actually asked.

The student identifies correctly that distance moved by the bubble in the potometer in a certain time is the variable that should be measured (the dependent variable).

The answer also mentions keeping other (control) variables constant. This is important to ensure that it is the independent variable which is affecting the dependent variable.

B Peer assessment

2 **Lipids are an important component of a balanced diet. Explain the importance of lipase and bile in the digestion of lipids.** [6]

Student answer

Lipase is a digestive enzyme which breaks down lipids into amino acids. Bile is an alkali secretion which is stored in the gall bladder. It is released into the small intestine where it neutralises hydrochloric acid, which has been released from the stomach. Its main function is to emulsify lipids. This means causing the lipids to become small droplets, which increases the surface area. This speeds up digestion by lipase because the enzyme has a larger surface area on which to act. The alkaline conditions also increase the breakdown of lipids by lipase.

Use the mark scheme and indicative content below to award this answer a level and a mark.

Mark scheme

Level	Description	Mark
Level 3	A clear, well-structured and logical answer where all the material is relevant. The answer clearly explains the importance of bile and lipase in the digestion of lipids with no key omissions or errors.	5–6
Level 2	A reasonably clear and logical answer with some structure, where most of the material is relevant. The importance of bile and lipase are both explained, but with omissions and some clear errors.	3–4
Level 1	Few relevant points, a lack of clear structure or logical reasoning. The answer is only a limited explanation of the importance of lipase or bile and contains obvious errors.	1–2
Level 0	No relevant content.	0

Indicative content:
- Lipase is a digestive enzyme which breaks down lipids, producing glycerol and fatty acids.
- The glycerol and fatty acids formed can then be used to produce new lipids.
- Bile is an alkaline secretion which is produced in the liver, stored in the gall bladder and acts in the small intestine.
- Bile neutralises stomach acid when it enters the duodenum.
- Bile emulsifies fat to form small droplets, which increases the surface area of the fat.
- The alkaline conditions and large surface area increase the rate of breakdown of the fat by lipase.

I would give this a level of .... and a mark of ....

This is because ...

....

....

....

C Improve the answer

3 An investigation was carried out into two groups of the fruit fly *Drosophila*. The flies from both groups are closely related, and were thought to be the same species. The observations made during the investigation are shown below.
- The two groups live in different areas.
- The groups feed on different food sources.
- Members of the same group can breed with each other and produce fertile offspring.
- A fly from one group can mate with a member of the other group, but cannot produce fertile offspring.

Use the concept of natural selection to explain these observations. [6]

Student answer

The flies are not members of the same species. This is because when they breed, they cannot produce fertile offspring. The theory of natural selection was proposed by Charles Darwin. It states that living things first developed from simple organisms millions of years ago. The fruit flies in the two groups were possibly the same species at one point. However, through 'survival of the fittest', the two groups changed – this was possibly due to different diets. Eventually, they became so different that they were no longer able to interbreed to produce fertile offspring.

Re-write this answer to improve it and obtain the full six marks.

Extended responses: Design/Plan

Both of these command words are used in a similar way, so they have been grouped together here. In a 'Design' or 'Plan' question, you would be asked to outline how you would carry out an investigation or study.

You should not worry about giving exact volumes or masses as part of the method, but should ensure your method is safe and appropriate to the context given. This means not including any equipment which would not be available, nor using an overly complex method.

Tip

In school microbiology investigations, an incubation temperature of 25°C would normally be used to prevent the growth of human pathogens. As this is an investigation carried out by a pharmaceutical company on a human pathogen, 37°C is an appropriate temperature to use.

A Expert commentary

1 A bacterial infection is proving resistant to common antibiotics such as penicillin. A pharmaceutical company would like to test the effect of the antibiotic tigecycline on the bacteria. Their hypothesis is that tigecycline will reduce the growth of the bacteria more than penicillin will.

Design an experiment, using discs soaked in antibiotics, to test this hypothesis. [6]

The details of the investigation are clearly laid out.

The end of the answer needs detail on comparing the results of the two antibiotics, and therefore concluding if the hypothesis is correct. The antibiotic which produces the largest clear area is the one which has reduced the growth of bacteria the most.

Student answer

Antibiotic solution of a known concentration and volume should be added to a series of discs. These discs should be placed on agar plates which contain a bacterial culture. The discs need to be placed in the centre of the agar plate. The plates then should be incubated at 37°C for 24 hours. At the end of this period, the clear area where no bacteria are growing should be measured.

This is a level 2 answer which would probably score three marks.

The key issue with this answer is that the hypothesis and the two different antibiotics are not referenced at all. It needs to be stated at the start of the answer that this method will be used for penicillin and tigecycline, and that the results can then be compared.

B Peer assessment

2 **A student was presented with three samples of food. They were asked to determine which one contained protein. Plan an investigation that would allow them to do this.** [4]

Student answer

The student would use the test for proteins, which is the biuret test. They should mix samples of each of the foods with biuret reagent, and check to see if there is a change of colour. If the biuret solution turns from blue to purple, this is shows that the food sample contains protein.

Use the mark scheme and indicative content below to award this answer a level and a mark.

Mark scheme

Level	Description	Mark
Level 3	A clear, well-structured and logical answer where all the material is relevant. The student clearly sets out the method for correctly identifying protein in a sample, including using biuret reagent, the colour change from blue to purple and ensuring the same mass or concentration of each sample is used.	3–4
Level 2	A reasonably clear and logical answer with some structure, where most of the material is relevant but with some key omissions.	1–2
Level 1	No relevant content.	0

Indicative content:
- Add a fixed volume of each sample to a fixed volume of biuret reagent.
- Observe the colour change that occurs.
- Samples that turn from blue to purple contain protein.
- Samples that remain blue do not contain protein.

I would give this a level of .... and a mark of ....

This is because ...

....

....

....

C Improve the answer

3 **A student was investigating the frequency of a *Taraxacum* species in a patch of wasteland which is approximately 200 m². They had access to the equipment below:**

- 0.25 m² quadrat
- 2 × 10 m tape measures
- random number generator.

Design an investigation to measure the population size of the *Taraxacum* species in the area. [6]

Student answer

First, set up the two tape measures to make a grid. Stand in the middle of the grid and throw the quadrat over your shoulder. Count how many *Taraxacum* are found in the quadrat and record this number. Use the random number generator to generate a number. Repeat the investigation this number of times, and calculate a mean number of *Taraxacum*. Multiply this number by 4 to give a mean number per m². You can then multiply this value by 200 to get an estimate of the population in the wasteland.

Re-write this answer to improve it and obtain the full six marks.

Extended responses: Justify

When answering a 'Justify' question, you need to use evidence in the question as well as your own scientific knowledge to justify why a particular course of action has been taken or conclusion drawn. The key to success in a 'Justify' question is using all the information given in the question fully.

A Expert commentary

1 **The table below details treatment strategies for measles. Justify these treatment strategies.** [6]

Vaccination	All young children are vaccinated against measles.
Treatment	Antibiotics should not be used to treat measles. Patients should be given plenty of fluids and made to rest. Patients suffering from measles should be kept away from public areas.

Student answer

The description of the use of the vaccination requires much greater detail.

More detail could be given on how measles is damaging, for example it can be fatal, how measles is spread, as well as relating these ideas to the importance of keeping sufferers away from public areas.

Vaccination is very important because it prevents people getting measles, which is a very damaging disease. Antibiotics should not be used because measles is a virus and antibiotics cannot be used to treat a viral disease. Fluids and rest are a better treatment than antibiotics for measles, and are the best treatment. The patients suffering from measles should be kept away from public areas as measles is very easily spread, and keeping people at home will reduce the spread.

The student gives a good justification for why antibiotics should not be used to treat measles.

This is a level 2 answer which would probably score three marks.

B Peer assessment

2 **A new drug that could be used to treat stroke has recently been discovered. The scientists involved are planning a clinical trial to test the drug:**

- Carry out preclinical testing in the lab using live animals.
- Double-blind clinical trials using a placebo will then be carried out. The first trial will use low doses of the drug. The next stage will use a range of different doses.

Justify each stage of the drug testing plan. [6]

Student answer

The preclinical testing in the lab using live animals is to see if the drug is safe and if it works – this is testing the toxicity and efficacy of the drug. The first clinical trials carried out using a low dose are to check to see if the drug is safe for human use and if it is effective. The next trial using a range of doses is to test what dose is effective. A double-blind trial is used so that neither the patient nor the scientists know if a particular patient has the drug or the placebo. This reduces the chance of bias affecting the results.

Use the mark scheme and indicative content below to award this answer a level and a mark.

Mark scheme

Level	Description	Mark
Level 3	A clear, well-structured and logical answer where all the material is relevant. The answer justifies the importance of each of the stages of the trial using evidence.	5–6
Level 2	A reasonably clear and logical answer with some structure, where most of the material is relevant. Correct justification is given for most of the stages of the trial, but there are some omissions or incorrect statements.	3–4
Level 1	Few relevant points, a lack of clear structure or logical reasoning. The answer contains limited justification for the trial, and has major omissions or errors.	1–2
Level 0	No relevant content.	0

Indicative content:
- Test the drug's efficacy and toxicity with live animals.
- The first clinical trials are carried out to determine if the drug is safe for human use, and if it is an effective treatment.
- The next clinical trial is carried out to determine the effective dose of the drug.
- Double-blind trials – where neither the patient nor the researcher knows if the patient has taken the drug or the placebo – reduce the risk of bias affecting the trial's results.

I would give this a level of .... and a mark of ....

This is because ...

....

....

....

C Improve the answer

3 A farmer wanted to increase the yield of crops grown in their greenhouse. The graph below shows the effect of light intensity on the rate of photosynthesis. The farmer decided to increase the temperature in the greenhouse, in addition to increasing the light intensity in the greenhouse.

Use the graph to justify the farmer's course of action. [6]

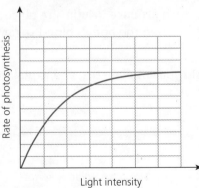

Student answer

Increasing light intensity increases the rate of photosynthesis. By increasing the light intensity in the greenhouse, the farmer will increase the amount of photosynthesis that their crops are doing, therefore they will grow more and the farmer will increase their yield. Temperature also effects the rate of photosynthesis, so by increasing the temperature the farmer will also increase the yield.

Re-write this answer to improve it and obtain the full six marks.

Extended responses: Evaluate

When answering an 'Evaluate' question, you should use your biological knowledge to consider the evidence of the statement given in the question. You should come to a conclusion about the statement – this will usually involve stating if a conclusion is correct or if the use of a particular process is valid.

(A) Expert commentary

1 A plant fungal disease was observed to begin in the lower leaves and move up into the leaves higher up a plant. It was not observed moving to leaves below the point at which the fungus was introduced. A scientist concluded that this evidence suggested the fungal disease was being transported in the phloem rather than the xylem.

Evaluate whether this conclusion uses the available evidence correctly. **[6]**

Student answer

The xylem transports minerals, ions and water up the plant. Xylem consist of tubes which contain lignin. The water moves up due to the transpiration stream. Phloem transports sugars made in photosynthesis from the leaves to the rest of the plant. This process is called translocation. The evidence given in the question suggests that the scientist is wrong, and the fungal disease is not moving by translocation.

This is a level 1 answer which would probably score two marks.

The functions of the xylem and phloem are described correctly.

The student comes to the correct conclusion that the scientist is incorrect, but this is not well explained.

While the conclusion is correct, the answer should make reference to the information about direction of the travel of the fungal disease, as given in the question.

The answer does not really answer the question. Most of the answer is just a description of xylem and phloem, with the fungal disease mentioned briefly at the end.

(B) Peer assessment

2 A new device has been developed to treat diabetes. Stem cells, which produce insulin, are placed on a chip which is implanted in a patient's body. Insulin is released when the body's blood sugar is too high. The device is currently awaiting a clinical trial.

Evaluate the effectiveness of this device in treating the different types of diabetes, and explain the importance of carrying out clinical trials. **[6]**

Student answer

The device could be useful when treating diabetes. Diabetes means that the pancreas will no longer produce insulin, which leads to the blood glucose concentration reaching too high levels. The implant will release insulin, which will cause the pancreas to convert the glucose into glycogen. This will cause the blood glucose concentration to fall to normal levels. This treatment could be particularly useful for obese people who are more likely to suffer from diabetes.

Clinical trials are trials of the treatment carried out on patients. They are important to test if the treatment is safe. In a treatment like this, it would be important to test to see if the implant was attacked by the body's immune system. They also test for efficacy – this means testing for how effective the treatment is. The results of these trials can then be published to allow peer review of the data.

Use the mark scheme and indicative content below to award this answer a level and a mark.

Mark scheme

Level	Description	Mark
Level 3	A clear, well-structured and logical answer where all the material is relevant. The student sets out clearly the effectiveness of the device in treating the two different types of diabetes, and clearly details the importance of a clinical trial.	5–6
Level 2	A reasonably clear and logical answer with some structure, where most of the material is relevant. The student sets out how the device can treat diabetes but fails to fully explain its suitability for treating both types of diabetes. They make some comments on the importance of clinical trials, but miss out some important details.	3–4
Level 1	Few relevant points, a lack of clear structure or logical reasoning. The student gives a limited explanation of the device's effectiveness in treating diabetes. and a limited explanation of the importance of clinical trials.	1–2
Level 0	No relevant content.	0

Indicative content:
- The treatment could be effective for patients with type 1 diabetes, as they do not produce insulin.
- The treatment would not be effective for patients with type 2 diabetes, as they do produce insulin but their cells no longer respond to it.
- When the patient's blood glucose concentration goes too high, the chip will release insulin.
- This will reduce the blood glucose concentration, and bring it back to normal levels.
- This treatment would remove the need for insulin injections.
- Clinical trials are important to determine safety of the treatment, or if there are any side effects.
- Trials can also be used to determine the optimum dose, and test the efficacy of the treatment.
- Double-blind trials with placebos can be used so that no one knows which patients are receiving the treatment and which are receiving the placebo.
- The data from the trial can be peer reviewed to determine if the conclusions drawn from the trial are correct.

I would give this a level of .... and a mark of ....

This is because ...

....

....

....

C Improve the answer

3 **Chlorosis is a plant condition which can be caused by a lack of chlorophyll and proteins. A gardener was finding that large numbers of their plants were suffering from this condition. They treated the plants by adding nitrate fertiliser.**

Evaluate the suitability of this treatment for the plants. **[6]**

Student answer

This should be a suitable treatment for the plants because the condition is caused by a lack of proteins, and nitrates are used by plants for protein synthesis. By adding nitrates to the soil, the plant will be able to take these in and use them for protein synthesis.

Re-write this answer to improve it and obtain the full six marks.

The guidance and activities in this Literacy section should have helped you get to grips with what you need to do in order to do well in extended response questions. Remember that there are more opportunities to practise what you've learnt here by using the exam-style papers provided (see page 98 and online).

3 Working Scientifically

Working scientifically is an area that is included as a required part of GCSE Biology, although you will never be asked specific questions that are labelled 'working scientifically' in the exam. In reality, being able to work scientifically is a skill and a way of thinking – namely thinking like a scientist. This mindset can be hard to get into, but once you start thinking this way, it will be an incredibly useful skill for both GCSE and if you take biology to A-level and beyond.

Most of the working scientifically skills will be covered as you work through your course. This section is all about making you aware of these skills, so that you can look out for where they feature in your studies, and use these opportunities to develop your thinking.

Working scientifically includes several different skills, which fall broadly into the following areas:

1 the development of scientific thinking

2 experimental skills and strategies

3 analysis and evaluation

4 vocabulary, units, symbols and nomenclature.

This section will deal with the first three areas, as vocabulary, units, symbols and nomenclature are covered in the Maths and Literacy sections of this book (see page 5 and page 45, respectively).

» Apparatus and techniques

As well as the four working scientifically areas, you are also required to demonstrate your capability in using a range of apparatus and techniques (AT skills). These are techniques that you will develop over your course as you complete the required practicals. In GCSE Biology, these are:

AT 1	Use of appropriate apparatus to make and record a range of measurements accurately, including length, area, mass, time, temperature, volume of liquids and gases, and pH.
AT 2	Safe use of appropriate heating devices and techniques, including use of a Bunsen burner and a water bath or electric heater.
AT 3	Use of appropriate apparatus and techniques for the observation and measurement of biological changes and/or processes.
AT 4	Safe and ethical use of living organisms (plants or animals) to measure physiological functions and responses to the environment.
AT 5	Measurement of rates of reaction by a variety of methods, including the production of gas, uptake of water and colour change of indicator.
AT 6	Application of appropriate sampling techniques to investigate the distribution and abundance of organisms in an ecosystem via direct use in the field.
AT 7	Use of appropriate apparatus, techniques and magnification – including microscopes – to make observations of biological specimens and produce labelled, scientific drawings.
AT 8	(single sciences only) – Use of appropriate techniques and qualitative reagents to identify biological molecules and processes in more complex and problem-solving contexts, including continuous sampling in an investigation.

Examples of how the AT skills might tie in to your learning are given below:

AT 1	• Record length and area when drawing and labelling cells, and when carrying out ecological sampling. • Record clear areas produced by antibiotics or antiseptics on bacterial cultures. • Record mass and time when investigating osmosis in plant tissues. • Record volumes, time, pH and temperature when investigating enzymes and rates of decay. • Record length and time when investigating factors that affect the growth of plants. • Record the rate of production of oxygen when investigating photosynthesis.
AT 2	• Use a Bunsen burner and boiling water safely when testing for non-reducing sugars. • Use a water bath safely to control temperature in enzyme and photosynthesis investigations.
AT 3	• Use transects and quadrats in ecological sampling. • Select appropriate apparatus to measure reaction times, bacterial growth, osmosis, the rate of photosynthesis or growth of plants.
AT 4	• Carry out ecological sampling safely and ethically. • Measure the responses of plants to different environmental factors safely and ethically. • Measure the responses of bacteria to antibiotics and antiseptics safely and ethically. • Carry out investigations into reaction times safely and ethically.
AT 5	• Measure the rate of water uptake in an osmosis investigation. • Measure the rate of an enzyme reaction using the colour change of an indicator. • Measure the rate of oxygen production in a photosynthesis investigation.
AT 6	• Investigate the abundance and distribution of organisms using transects and quadrats.
AT 7	• Make observations and produce labelled, scientific drawings when investigating plant growth and when using a light microscope.
AT 8	• Use qualitative reagents in tests for carbohydrates, proteins and lipids.

» Development of scientific thinking

This section covers how scientific thinking develops, which includes how theories evolve over time, the use of different models as a way of understanding concepts and the ethical issues associated with scientific research and methods. It also covers the importance of peer review and communicating scientific ideas.

How theories develop over time

The scientific method is the process of formulating a hypothesis and then testing it by carrying out investigations. The results of these investigations can then be used to check the hypothesis, and either reject or refine it. Successful hypotheses can then be used to develop theories which explain natural phenomena.

You could be asked to give examples of how specific scientific methods and theories have developed over time. This could include how new data from experiments or observations have led to these developments. You could also be presented with some data, and asked if it that data supports a particular theory.

A key example of the development of a theory in biology is the theory of evolution over time, outlined below:

Charles Darwin used his own observations, experimentation and the developing knowledge of geology and fossils to develop his theory of evolution. Darwin's theory was extremely controversial, and it was only as new evidence became available – including the mechanisms of inheritance – that it became widely accepted. The evidence helped disprove alternative theories such as those of

> **Key terms**
>
> **Scientific method:** The formulation, testing and modification of hypotheses by systematic observation, measurement and experiment.
>
> **Hypothesis:** A proposed explanation for a phenomenon used as a starting point for further testing.
>
> **Phenomenon:** An observation that prompts you to ask questions. The plural of phenomenon is phenomena.

other scientists like Jean-Baptiste Lamarck, who believed that changes during a single organism's lifetime could be inherited by their offspring. New discoveries, for example in the field of epigenetics, mean that our understanding of evolution will continue to develop.

Using biological models

There is an enormous range of models used in biology to help us explain and understand different concepts. These models can be divided into four categories:

1 Representational – these models describe a particular thing using shapes or analogies. For example, a model of the structure of a DNA molecule.
2 Mathematical – these models use data and calculations to make predictions. For example, using equations to model bacterial growth.
3 Descriptive – these models describe the features of a system and how they interact. For example, a description of the carbon cycle.
4 Computational – these are mathematical models run by a computer. For example, a computer model might be used to show the spread of an infectious disease in a population.

Models of the function of organ systems such as the circulatory system or respiratory system are often used in GCSE Biology. The simplest of these could be to use a bell jar to model pressure and volume changes in the lungs.

> **Tip**
>
> You could be asked to give the limitations of a particular model. All models have some limitations as they are always an imperfect representation of reality. The key to a successful model is one that is representative enough without being too complex.

Appreciating the limitations of science and ethical issues

Science is an incredibly powerful tool to help us understand our world and also improve people's lives. However, it is only a tool, which means it has limits – both those imposed by the natural world and what is realistically achievable, and also limits that we impose ourselves. Often, the limits we impose ourselves are because of ethical concerns. We need to constantly evaluate our use of science and decide whether any particular piece of scientific research is the 'right' thing to do.

Ethical issues run through many different areas of biology. For example, one key ethical decision involves the use of living organisms in investigations. Exam questions may ask you to consider the ethical issues arising from a particular piece of research that involves killing the animal. In your answer to these types of questions, you might discuss ideas around an organism's 'right to life' balanced against the potential benefits of the research.

> **Key term**
>
> Ethical issues: Issues where a choice needs to be made between different options that are viewed as morally right (ethical) or wrong (unethical).

Other ethical issues also arise in biology when considering cloning, IVF or the use of stem cells. These issues centre around the perceived rights of an embryo – some people believe that an embryo has a right to life, while other people believe that because an early embryo could not survive outside its mother, it is not truly alive, and therefore the benefits that derive from their use outweigh the ethical issues against their use.

Understanding the everyday and technological applications of science

You can see the impact of science all around you every day and everywhere you look. In the exam, you may be asked to describe examples of the technological applications of science within the biology specification.

Some of the example applications in your specification may include:

- treating coronary heart disease and heart failure, namely the use of stents to keep the coronary arteries open, and statins to reduce blood cholesterol levels
- vaccinations to reduce the spread of pathogens, and the importance of immunising a large proportion of the population
- detecting, identifying and treating plant diseases such as the tobacco mosaic virus and black spot
- the environmental implications of deforestation, global warming and a loss of habitats leading to a decrease in biodiversity
- fishing techniques, and how they can promote the recovery of fish stocks by controlling net size and introducing fishing quotas.

Exam questions on this area may ask you to evaluate methods that can be used to tackle the issues described in the question.

Evaluating the risks in science

Whenever scientists do practical work, they need to evaluate any potential risks and complete all practical investigations safely. At GCSE, you should have carried out risk assessments when doing required practicals, but you could also be asked to identify hazards in an exam question.

To complete a risk assessment successfully, you need to:

- identify the hazard and risk
- decide the likelihood of the incident actually happening
- suggest ways of reducing the risk of potential harm.

An example of a risk assessment for the test for reducing sugar is outlined below.

Table 3.1 **Risk assessment**

Hazard	Risk	How to reduce risk
Benedict's solution is an irritant.	There is a risk Benedict's solution could come into contact with skin or eyes.	Wear safety goggles to prevent Benedict's solution from entering eyes. If Benedict's solution comes into contact with skin, wash affected area immediately.

When giving methods of reducing risk, you should ensure that you are specific, and reduce risks presented by that particular practical. Make sure you avoid general statements like 'work safely'.

Recognising the importance of peer review

New scientific research is often published in scientific journals. This research is peer reviewed before it is published. Peer review is a process by which scientific research is checked (and validated) by other scientists. As part of this process, a paper will usually outline what the scientists were hoping to achieve, their methods, results and their conclusions. This paper will then be peer reviewed by independent experts to ensure that the research has been carried out correctly, that results are logical and that they support any conclusions drawn.

This ensures that a piece of research is valid and is vital to the development of scientific knowledge, particularly in achieving wider agreement and recognition, and identifying false claims.

Tip

Details of how to answer 'Evaluate' questions can be found on page 56.

Key term

Peer review: The process by which experts in the same area of study evaluate the findings of another scientist before it is considered for inclusion in a scientific publication.

In most cases, media representations of science are not peer reviewed, and can give a biased or inaccurate viewpoint. This can lead to very real problems. For example, the rise in measles cases was caused by the drop in uptake of the MMR vaccine following untrue media reports of a false link with autism.

Questions

1. What is the scientific method?
2. Explain how the theory of evolution has developed over time.
3. Why are models important in biology?
4. Give two examples of the use of models in biology.
5. How is the technical application of biology helping to reduce the impact of overfishing?
6. During IVF, some embryos are destroyed. Explain why some people may have objections to IVF.
7. Write a risk assessment for an investigation where the main hazard is the use of hydrochloric acid.
8. Explain how the peer review process can identify claims based on false data.
9. What are the advantages of sharing results in a class practical?

Tip

Peer review can be seen on a small-scale within your own class – sharing practical results with other students allows you to see if your results are consistent, and are therefore reproducible (see pages 68–69 for details on reproducibility).

» Experimental skills and strategies

As we have already seen, investigations are usually designed to test a hypothesis as part of the scientific method. The investigation is carried out, results are collected and the hypothesis is evaluated. This section covers the key areas needed to complete a successful investigation.

Developing scientific theories and hypotheses

A hypothesis is a proposed explanation for a phenomenon, and is used as a starting point for further testing. For example, when investigating the action of protease, a possible hypothesis might be:

Increasing the surface area of a sample of protein increases the rate at which the protein is broken down by protease.

This hypothesis could then be tested by conducting an investigation which measures the effect of different surface areas of proteins on the rate at which they are broken down by protease.

In both the exam and in a required practical, you could be given some data and asked to suggest a hypothesis to explain the trend shown. Look carefully at the data, consider what part of your scientific knowledge it relates to and use this scientific knowledge to suggest the most likely hypothesis.

Planning experiments to test hypotheses

In the exam, you could be asked to design or outline a practical procedure to test a particular hypothesis. To do this, you will need to use your own knowledge of the practicals you have completed and any information given in the question. You should also be able to explain why your chosen method is suitable for testing that specific hypothesis, and know why each of the steps needs to be carried out.

When designing a practical investigation, you need to make sure that you are only changing one thing at a time as part of your tests. If you change more than one thing at once, it will be impossible to know which of the things you changed

Tip

Remember that your hypothesis should not be too outlandish or surprising – make sure you sense-check what you have written. At GCSE, the questions will likely lead you to a fairly obvious answer.

caused the results to be different, or even if both had an effect. The things that you can change are called 'variables'. There are three different types:

- Independent variable – this is the variable that is changed by the person doing the practical.
- Dependent variable – this is the variable that is measured during the investigation. We think that this variable is affected by (or dependent on) changes in the independent variable.
- Control variables – these are variables that could affect the dependent variable. They need to be kept constant to ensure that it is only the independent variable causing any changes in the dependent variable.

Knowing what hypothesis you are testing for will affect which variable you decide to change, which you need to measure and which ones you need to keep the same (for control) to make it a fair test. That is why knowing what each of the variables means will help you to plan experiments.

For example, in an investigation to assess the effect of pH on the rate of an enzyme catalysed reaction, you would have the following variables:

- independent variable – pH of solution (this is the factor that you want to investigate)
- dependent variable – rate of reaction (this will be measured during the investigation to see if and how it is affected by the independent variable – the pH of solution)
- control variables – all other variables that could affect the rate of an enzyme catalysed reaction should be controlled. These could include temperature, substrate concentration or enzyme concentration. This will lead to the test being fair.

> **Tip**
> ●
> For some practicals in biology, you may have a controlled experiment to help you see the impact of changing an independent variable. For example, in an enzyme investigation a boiled and cooled enzyme is often used as a control. The experiment is repeated with all other variables kept the same as the main investigation, but this control investigation won't produce any results as the enzyme has been denatured and will no longer catalyse the reaction.

> **Tip**
> ● ● ● ● ● ● ● ● ● ● ●
> These types of questions usually contain the command words 'Design' or 'Plan'. See pages 52–53 for more detail on these command words.

> **Key terms**
>
> Independent variable: The variable selected to be changed by an investigator.
>
> Dependent variable: The variable measured during an investigation.
>
> Control variables: Variables other than the independent variable which could affect the dependent variable, and are therefore kept constant and unchanged.
>
> Fair test: A test in which there is one independent variable, one dependent variable and all other variables are controlled.

> **Tip**
> ● ● ● ● ● ● ● ● ● ● ●
> You may also get asked to identify the different sorts of variable in an exam question.

Choosing appropriate techniques, apparatus and materials

When completing practical experiments or questions, you may be asked what the best technique, instrument, apparatus or material would be for a particular purpose. You should think carefully about your choice and be prepared to justify it.

Below are some questions to consider when making your choice of technique:

- Will this technique collect the data required by the investigation?
- Is the technique precise enough?
- Is it realistic to use this technique in this context?

For example:

- In investigations involving photosynthesis by aquatic plants, the rate of gas produced can be measured by counting bubbles produced in a certain amount of time. However, this is not a very precise measure of the volume of gas produced. A better technique would be to change the apparatus and use a gas syringe to give a much more precise measure of volume.

- When measuring very small volumes of liquid, a graduated pipette or syringe would be more appropriate than using a measuring cylinder.
- The use of complex equipment, such as laser measuring devices or electron microscopes, is unlikely to be realistic in the context of a question asking you to design an investigation to be carried out in a school lab.

Some common apparatus that you might use in biology are outlined in the table below.

Table 3.2 Common apparatus

Apparatus	What the apparatus is used to measure
Measuring cylinder / dropper pipette / syringe / graduated pipette	Measuring the volume of liquid Note: Generally, a graduated pipette would be the most precise out of these pieces of apparatus, and the dropper pipette would be the least precise.
Balance	Measuring mass
Gas syringe	Measuring the volume of gas
Potometer	Measuring the rate of water uptake by a plant

Carrying out experiments appropriately and accurately

Planning is important in carrying out experiments appropriately. If you do not plan out an experiment properly, it can lead to results not being accurate or precise enough to draw reasoned conclusions. This is called an 'error in methodology', and is different from carrying out the experimental techniques incorrectly.

To ensure you avoid these types of errors, you need to think about potential issues in specific experiments. For example:

- If using a thermostatically-controlled water bath, ensure that there is time for the sample in the water bath to reach the same temperature as the water bath. Students often put test tubes into a water bath and begin collecting results immediately. This is incorrect as the contents of the test tube will take time to reach the desired temperature.
- When carrying out an investigation involving living organisms, you should allow any organisms to acclimatise to their surroundings before beginning to take measurements. This is because organisms will often be stressed by being moved or put into new surroundings, and this may affect the variable you are attempting to measure.

It is also really important to ensure that the equipment you select is accurate enough to gather the data required, for example, if the differences in mass between two samples is likely to be very small, you should ensure the balance you are using is precise enough to distinguish this small change. When picking your equipment, it is useful to think about the differences between accuracy, reliability, precision and resolution.

Tip

It can be quite easy to get these terms confused, so make sure you are clear on their definitions and how they are different.

Accuracy

Accuracy is how close we are to the true value of a measurement. The best way to improve accuracy is to use more accurate measuring equipment, for example, a graduated pipette will measure the volume of a solution to a greater degree of accuracy than a measuring cylinder.

Resolution

Resolution is the fineness to which an instrument can be read. For example, a simple thermometer may have a resolution of 1 °C, which means it can measure to the nearest °C. A digital temperature probe could have a resolution of 0.01 °C. This means the probe can measure to the nearest 0.01 °C and therefore has a much higher resolution than the thermometer.

> **Key term**
> Resolution: The fineness to which an instrument can be read.

Precision

Precise measurements are those where the range is small. For example, in an investigation into temperature change, a student measured the temperature change on one thermometer labelled 'A' and got the following results: 3 °C, 7 °C and 6 °C. The range of these measurements is $7 - 3 = 4$ °C, and the mean is 5 °C.

The exact same experiment was then carried out with another thermometer labelled 'B' and got the following results: 4 °C, 6 °C and 6 °C. The range of these measurements is $6 - 4 = 2$ °C, but the mean is still 5 °C, as in thermometer 'A'. Although they both have the same mean value, thermometer 'B' has greater precision.

> **Key term**
> Precision: Precise measurements are those where the range is small.

Reliability

A test is defined as reliable if different scientists repeating the same experiment consistently get the same results. The technique to improve reliability is to repeat the same test several times.

> **Key term**
> Reliability: When different people repeat the same experiment and get the same results.

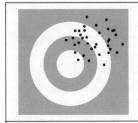  

These results are neither accurate (they are far from the bull's eye) nor precise (they are far apart from each other).	These results are precise (close together), but not accurate (they are far from the bull's eye).	These results are both accurate and precise.

▲ Figure 3.1 Diagram showing the meaning of accuracy and precision

Sampling techniques

When gathering sample data, it is important to ensure that the data is representative. This means that the sample data collected is typical of the overall area being sampled.

This skill is especially important during ecological sampling. When investigating abundance of a plant in a field, you will be sampling a small area of the field and then using your sample results to estimate total abundance in the field. It is therefore very important that the area you are sampling is representative of the rest of the field. Below is a possible method that should produce representative results:

> **Key term**
> Representative data: Sample data which is typical of the overall area or population being sampled.

- Select a sample area, for example 10 m by 10 m and mark it out with a grid.
- Use a random number generator to generate co-ordinates of where to place your quadrats.
- Sample at least 10 quadrats in the sample area.
- Repeat the process in other sample areas in the field.

Taking multiple random samples in each sample area and using more than one sample area increases the chance of your results being representative of the field as a whole.

Tip

See pages 19–20 for more on sampling as it relates to mathematical calculations.

Making and recording observations and measurements

This is an important skill when carrying out practical activities, and it is important that you make and record measurements carefully, as well as double-checking them to ensure you have not made an error when reading off a scale.

You also need to make sure you plan to collect data in a timely fashion. If a reaction is occurring quickly, collecting data every five minutes might be inappropriate as the changes you are attempting to measure are occurring too fast. Similarly, if a process is occurring quite slowly, measuring every thirty seconds may be an inefficient use of time, and generate lots of data points that are not useful.

Some other common issues with making observations and measurements to look out for include:

- Failing to note the measurement correctly – either through misunderstanding what the scale is showing or through misreading it. To avoid this, make sure you are clear on what the scale is showing, including what the minor graduations represent, for example what the lines between $10\,cm^3$ and $20\,cm^3$ on a measuring cylinder represent.
- Not using a stopwatch correctly – ensure you are confident using the stopwatch you have been given – including starting, stopping and clearing it. Make sure you are able to start the stopwatch at the appropriate time and finish it precisely at the correct end point.
- Not zeroing a balance before measuring mass – ensure the balance reads zero before measuring a mass. This can involve placing a container on the balance, zeroing it and then placing the sample into the container. Failing to do this can mean that the mass you measure is the sample as well as the container it is being weighed in.
- Not accurately determining a colour change – measuring colour change is generally subjective due to the fact that different people may judge the final end point slightly differently. To help with this, you should use a reference sample which has already reached the end point of the colour change.

Tip

A **parallax error** can cause you to misread a scale. To avoid this type of error, make sure your eye is level with the measurement apparatus so that your line of sight is consistent.

Key term

Parallax error: A difference in the apparent value or position of an object caused by different lines of sight.

Evaluating methods and suggesting possible improvements

Evaluation is an important skill in science because no experiment or method is ever perfect. You should be evaluating your method constantly while conducting practicals, but you may also be asked to evaluate as part of exam questions.

Evaluating may involve assessing whether:

- sufficient, precise measurements have been taken in an experiment – if an experimental method lacks precision, it may produce results that are not valid

Tip

See page 56 for further examples of 'Evaluate' questions.

- the method used in the investigation could be improved – you should be able to justify your answer and suggest improvements to ensure the results of an investigation are valid.

When answering evaluation questions, you should consider the following:

- Did the measurements taken provide data which can be used to answer the hypothesis that the investigation set out to address convincingly?
- Are there any weaknesses in the experimental method or the conclusion drawn from the results?
- Are there any improvements that could be made to the experimental method which would have produced more accurate or precise data?
- Will any follow-up experiments be needed to address any further issues raised by the original investigation?

Questions

1 What is a hypothesis?
2 An investigation was carried out into the effect of light intensity on the rate of photosynthesis of a sample of pondweed. A light was placed at a range of distances from the pondweed and at each distance, the number of bubbles released from the pondweed in 5 minutes was counted. The same species and mass of pondweed was used throughout the investigation.
   a Identify the following variables in this investigation:
      i independent variable
      ii dependent variable
      iii two control variables.
   b Evaluate the method used in this investigation, and suggest an improvement.
3 What is representative data?
4 How do errors in methodology differ from errors made while carrying out an investigation?
5 Why is it important to allow organisms used in investigations to acclimatise to new surroundings?
6 Why is it important to not begin collecting results immediately after placing a sample in a water bath?
7 If investigating the abundance of a plant in a field, why is it important to take a number of different samples?

>> Analysis and evaluation

Once experimental results have been collected, they need to be presented, analysed and then evaluated so that you can write a reasoned conclusion.

Collecting, presenting and analysing data

- It is very important to present data collected in an investigation as clearly as possible. This means ensuring that results tables and graphs are drawn correctly.
- Once data has been collected, further mathematical analysis can be carried out.

For more details on graphs, tables, distributions and analysing data, see the mathematical skills section.

Evaluating data

Evaluating the quality of data obtained in an investigation is very important because poor quality data may mean that any conclusions drawn from it are incorrect. When evaluating the quality of data collected in an investigation, you can talk about accuracy, precision, repeatability and reproducibility, but you should also consider uncertainty and errors that may have been made in the experiment.

Uncertainty

Whenever measurements are made in an investigation, there is always uncertainty about the results obtained. This uncertainty can be due to both the equipment and the experimental procedures used. Investigations can be improved to reduce the uncertainty of results, for example by using more precise equipment.

The range around the mean can be used as a measure of uncertainty. For example, if the range around the mean is quite small (for example the results are close to the mean) then the uncertainty of the results will be less than if the range around the mean is larger (the results are further from the mean). If the range is large, it is important you take this uncertainty into account when evaluating the data and deciding whether it is suitable enough to use as a basis for a conclusion.

Uncertainty can be represented on a graph by range bars. The larger the range bars, the more uncertain the results.

Types of error

As well as taking into account uncertainty, your data evaluation should consider whether there were any likely errors in measurements. There are two main types of errors to look at:

- Random error – these cause measurements to differ from the true value by different amounts each time – in other words, where results vary in unpredictable ways. This is a particular problem in biology because living organisms show a high degree of variation. For example, when measuring reaction times, one value may be very different from another due to the subject being distracted. Random errors can be reduced by making more measurements and reporting a mean value (see pages 14–15 for details on calculating means).
- Systematic error – these cause measurements to differ from the true value by the same amount each time. Systematic errors are therefore generally caused by problems with equipment or the experimental procedure. For example, if a balance has an error of 0.5 g, then all of the masses measured by this balance would differ from the true value by 0.5 g. If systematic errors are known about, they can be taken into account when analysing results.

> **Tip**
>
> Anomalous results are values that are very different to the rest of the results from an investigation. If they have been produced by incorrect measurement, then they can be ignored when calculating means or carrying out further analysis.

Repeatability, reproducibility and validity

When analysing results, they should also be ideally repeatable, reproducible and valid to ensure that they are useful.

- Results are repeatable if similar results are obtained when the investigation is repeated under the same conditions by the same investigator.
- Results are reproducible if similar results are obtained by different investigators using different equipment.
- Results are considered valid if the data is a correct measure of the property being investigated. For example, measuring the temperature change of a leaf over time would not be a valid measure of the rate of photosynthesis.

Reliable results are valid, repeatable and reproducible.

Reliable results are important in assessing whether we have discovered something meaningful. If results were, for example, repeatable but not reproducible, or reproducible but not valid, the results may be incorrect.

SCIENTIFIC VOCABULARY, QUANTITIES, UNITS AND SYMBOLS

Results that are just repeatable but not reproducible or valid are particularly suspect because the investigator may be repeating the same mistakes again and again. Reproducible results give greater confidence that they are correct because several people or techniques are involved. However, the results will only be valid if an appropriate variable is being investigated.

Tip

Measurements can be repeatable but still subject to errors caused by the equipment used or by the investigator's experimental technique. Reproducible results are less likely to contain such errors because the results are gathered using different equipment and by different investigators.

Questions

1   How does precision differ from accuracy?
2   What are anomalous results?
3   In an investigation into human reaction time, the below data was collected.

Reaction time (s)	1.2	1.3	1.1	1.2	1.1

A more detailed follow-up investigation calculated a mean reaction time of 0.5 seconds. What statement can be made about the results of the first investigation? Use the terms 'precise' and 'accurate' in your answer.
4   If the range of repeat results around the mean is large, what can be concluded about the level of uncertainty in the results?
5   What is the difference between random errors and systematic errors?
6   Explain how you could reduce random errors.
7   What steps could you take to reduce systematic errors in an investigation?
8   Explain the difference between the terms 'repeatability' and 'reproducibility'.
9   Why are reproducible results less likely to contain systematic errors than results that are just repeatable?
10   What do large range bars on a graph indicate?

» Scientific vocabulary, quantities, units and symbols

Scientific vocabulary

Using correct scientific vocabulary in exam answers is extremely important. You should learn the definitions of key words and technical terms and be comfortable using them. When answering exam questions, always consider whether you have written the best possible answer or could you use more key words and scientific vocabulary? For information on scientific vocabulary used in biology, refer to the Literacy section of this book (see page 45).

Scientific quantities, units and symbols

For information on the quantities and units used in science, as well as how to convert between them, refer to the Maths section of this book (see page 5).

4 Revision skills

This section covers the importance of revision and the key strategies that can help you gain the most benefit from your revision. A common misconception is that there is only one way to revise – one that involves lots of note-taking, re-reading and highlighting. However, research shows that this is not an effective way of revising. You need to vary the techniques you use – and find the ones that work best for *you* – to make the most of revision.

Students often think they can change the way they revise, or that revision is something you either can or cannot do. In fact, revision is an important skill and, like any skill, with support and practice you can get better at it. By 'better', this means that you can revise more efficiently (in other words, you'll get a greater benefit from the same amount of revision time) and more effectively (in other words, you'll retain more information).

This chapter will cover the key elements of successful revision:

- Planning ahead
- Using the right tools
- Creating the right environment
- Useful revision techniques
- Practice, practice, practice!

>> Planning ahead

The key to successful revision is planning. There are a number of things to bear in mind when planning revision.

Be realistic

There is nothing more demotivating than setting unrealistic targets and then not fulfilling them. You need to think carefully about how much work you can realistically complete and set a reasonable time to complete it.

Ensure you cover all topics in the course

It is tempting to focus on what you think are the most important areas and leave out others. This is risky because no one knows what you will be asked about. It's a horrible feeling seeing an exam question on a topic that you know you haven't revised. In this section, there is advice on the sorts of strategies to ensure you cover all the key points of the specification.

Make friends with the areas you don't like

It is tempting to focus on the areas you already know and are good at. It makes you feel like you're making great progress when, in fact, you're doing yourself a disservice. You should work hard at the areas you find difficult to make sure you give yourself the best chance. This can be tough as you may feel progress is slow, but you must persevere with it.

> **Tip**
> Spend a small amount of time each evening during your GCSE course going over what you learnt in that day's lesson – it can be really beneficial. It helps you remember the content when you come to revise it, and provides good preparation for the next lesson.

Ask for help

The most successful students are often those who ask questions from teachers, parents and other students. If there is anything on the specification that you are unsure about, don't stay silent – ask a question! Proper planning will ensure you have time to ask these questions as you work through your revision.

Target setting

Targets are an important part of successful revision planning. You may want to include SMART targets in your revision timetable.

Here's an example of a SMART (specific, measurable, achievable, realistic and timely) target.

Target: Achieve at least a grade 6 in a practice Chemistry Paper 1 done under exam conditions. This should be completed by the end of the week.

- **Specific** – this target is specific as it gives the exam paper, how it needs to be completed and the grade required.
- **Measurable** – as a specific minimum grade is given (6), this target is measurable.
- **Achievable** – as long as there is time to complete the paper, which there should be if it's being completed in the 'time allowed', then this target would be achievable.
- **Realistic** – you shouldn't be expecting to score grade 9 in assessments straight away or learn huge amounts of content in a very small time; so, a grade 6 seems to be realistic for a first stab.
- **Timely** – there is a set time to complete this goal, namely by the end of the week. Assuming that the student has revised all of the topics on this paper by then, this is a sensible timeframe.

Targets can also be smaller and set for individual revision sessions, for example:

- complete three practice questions on one maths skill
- get 75% on a recall test
- learn the stages of a process, e.g. the carbon cycle
- make a set of key word flash cards on Lenses and Visible Light

Setting targets for each revision session will help you realise when you are finished, as well as providing yourself with evidence of your progress – always a good motivator!

> **Tip**
> Targets can include things such as not using social media or your phone for a whole revision session if this is something you particularly struggle with.

›› Using the right tools

Having the right tools is vital for effective revision. Some of the 'practical' tools you'll need during your revision would include:

- a planner or diary
- pens
- paper
- highlighters
- flash cards
- and so on ...

Having these tools close to hand will remove simple barriers to successful revision – such as not having a pen!

Revision timetables

Revision timetables are a useful tool to help you organise and structure your work. Remember that the key is to be realistic – don't plan to do too much, or you'll become demoralised.

Revision works best in shorter blocks. So, don't plan to spend two hours solidly revising one topic – you probably won't last that long. Even if you do, it's unlikely the work towards the end of this time will be effective. Techniques that help with useful, timely revision are covered in more detail on pages 75–76.

If you are making a revision timetable for mock exams (before you've finished your course), you will need to allow time for any homework set in addition to revision.

How to create a revision timetable

Identify the long-term goal and short-term targets you're trying to achieve (and make sure they're SMART). Ask yourself if this a general timetable to use during the term, or one aimed at preparing for a particular exam or assessment. This will affect how you build your plan as your commitments will vary.

Whatever the end goal, don't plan so you only just finish in time. Make sure you plan to cover all the topic areas you need well before the assessment. That way, if you encounter problems that slow you down, you won't run out of time.

Examples of revision timetables

Good example

Revision sessions split into small sections. This helps maintain engagement during the session.

Regular breaks scheduled and a realistic expectations of how much revision can be completed in a day.

Times	Mon
8:30am–3:20pm	School
4:00pm–4:30pm	Chemistry (size and mass of atoms)
4:30pm–5:30pm	Football
5:30pm–6:00pm	Dinner
6:00pm–6:30pm	Physics (black body radiation)
6:30pm–7:00pm	Online gaming
7:00pm–7:30pm	Biology (meiosis)

Bad example

Unrealistic expectations – timetabling so revision starts at 6:30 am and finishes at 11:00 pm at night is unrealistic and potentially harmful. Failing to achieve set goals can be very demotivating.

Working excessive long hours without adequate sleep and relaxation time can be detrimental to health.

Times	Mon
6:30am–7:20am	Physics
8:30am–3:30pm	School
3:30pm–5:00pm	Physics
5:00pm–7:30pm	Chemistry
7:30pm–11:00pm	Biology

No breaks scheduled – planning breaks, both as a rest and reward, are very important for effective revision.

Tip

Include your other commitments in a revision timetable, such as music lessons, sports, exercise or part time work. This will give a clearer picture of how much time you have for revision. These commitments could be rewards – they give you something look forward to. Or it may become clear that you may have too much on and have to (temporarily) give something up.

Tip

Make sure you carefully plan how much time you have available before each exam. Miscalculating by even a week could cause problems.

Specific topics given for revision sections – while you don't need to necessarily rigidly stick to this it's good to have a topic focus for each revision session, you can then set targets for the session based around this particular topic area.

No specific topics mentioned – 'Physics' is far too vague; what areas are they specifically going to work on?

Long blocks of one subject – the student is unlikely to remain engaged for this length of time.

Revision checklist

A revision checklist is an important tool to ensure you are covering all the required specification content. Your teacher may provide you with a revision checklist, but even if they do, making one yourself can be a useful learning activity.

Tip

Some revision guides (like *My Revision Notes*) also have checklists included that you can use.

How to make a revision checklist

1 Read the specification; this is everything you need to know.
2 Split the specification into short statements and place them into a grid.
3 Work through the grid, ticking as you complete each stage for a particular topic. Use practice exam questions to check that your revision has been effective.
4 Return to the areas you are weaker in and focus on improving them.

Example revision checklist

The following is an example statement taken from a GCSE Physics specification. This statement has been used as the basis for an example revision checklist.

Learners should have a knowledge and awareness of the advantages and disadvantages of renewable energy technologies (e.g. hydroelectric, wind power, wave power, tidal power, waste, solar, wood) for generating electricity. Learners should also be able to explain the advantages and disadvantages of non-renewable energy technologies, including fossil fuels and nuclear for generating electricity.

Revision checklist

Specification statement	Covered in class	Revised	Completed example questions	Questions to ask teacher
Advantages and disadvantages of renewable energy resources for generating electricity 1 – hydroelectric, wind power, wave power, tidal power.				
Advantages and disadvantages of renewable energy resources for generating electricity 2 – waste, solar, wood.				
Advantages and disadvantages of fossil fuels for generating electricity.				
Advantages and disadvantages of nuclear power for generating electricity.				

Posters

You could create posters of key processes, diagrams and points and put them up around the house so you can revise throughout the day. Be sure to change the posters regularly so that you don't become too used to them and they lose their impact. See the next section for more on making the most of your learning environment.

Technology

There are many ways to use technology to help you revise. For example, you can make slideshows of key points, watch short videos or listen to podcasts. The advantage of creating a resource yourself is that it forces you to think about a particular topic in detail. This will help you to remember key points and improve your understanding. The finished products should be kept safe so you can revisit them closer to the exam. You could lend your products to friends and borrow ones they've made to share the workload.

Tip

Don't procrastinate by focusing too much on the appearance of your notes. It can be tempting to spend large amounts of time making revision timetables and notes that look nice, but this is a distraction from the real work of revising.

Making your own video and audio

If you record yourself explaining a particular concept or idea, either as a video or podcast, you can listen to it whenever you want. For example, while travelling to or from school. But make sure your explanation is correct, or you may reinforce incorrect information.

Revision slideshows

Slideshows can incorporate diagrams, videos and animations from the internet to aid your understanding of complex processes. They can be converted into video files, printed out as posters, or viewed on screen. It's important to focus on the content of the slideshow – don't spend too long making it look nice.

Social media

Social media contain a wide range of revision resources. However, it is important to make sure resources are correct. If it's user-generated content, there's no guarantee the information will be accurate.

Study vloggers and other students on social media can provide valuable support and a sense of being part of a wider community going through the same pressures as you. However, don't compare yourself to other people in case it makes you feel as if you're not keeping up.

» Creating the right environment

The importance of having a suitable environment to revise in cannot be underestimated – you can have the best plan and intentions in the world, but if you're watching TV at the same time, or you can't find the book you need, or you're gasping for a drink and so on, then you're likely to lose concentration sooner rather than later. Make sure you create a sensible working space.

Work area and organisation

It is difficult to concentrate with the distraction of an untidy work area – so keep it tidy! It is also inefficient, as you may spend time looking for things you've mislaid.

The importance of organisation extends to your exercise books and revision folders. You will have at least two years' worth of work to revise and study. Misplacing work can have a negative effect on your revision.

Put together a revision folder with all your notes, practice questions, checklists, timetables and so on. You could organise it by topic so it's easy to find particular information and see the work you have already completed.

Looking after yourself

Revising for exams is a marathon, not a sprint – you don't want to burn out before you reach the exams. Make sure you stay healthy and happy while revising. This is important for your own wellbeing, and helps you revise effectively.

Eat properly

Try to eat a healthy, balanced diet. Keep some healthy snacks nearby so that hunger doesn't distract you when revising. Food high in sugar is not ideal for maintaining concentration, so make sure you're sensible when selecting snacks.

> **Tip**
>
> Be aware that social media can also be distracting. It's easy to procrastinate if you're not focused. Advice on reducing distractions can found on page 75.

> **Tip**
>
> Some students find listening to music helpful when they're revising, even associating certain artists or songs with specific topics. However, music can also be distracting, so only use it if it works for you.

Drink plenty of water

Make sure you have enough water at hand to last your revision session. It's vital to stay hydrated and getting up to get a drink can be a distraction, particularly if you wander past the TV on the way.

Consider when you work most effectively

Different people work better at different times of the day (morning, afternoon, early evening). Try to plan your revision during the times you're most productive. This may take some trial and error at the start of your revision.

Make sure you get enough sleep

Lack of sleep can lead to serious health problems. Late-night cramming is not an effective revision technique.

Avoiding distractions

Social media and other technology can provide an unwelcome temptation when studying. Possible solutions to this distraction include:

Plan specific online activities during study breaks

This could be social media time, videos or gaming. This can also give you something to look forward to while you're working. Be careful to ensure you stick to the allotted break time and don't fall into the trap of 'just one more' video or game.

Switch technology off

Switching the internet off can be the most powerful productivity tool. Turn off your phone and consider avoiding the internet whilst studying, only turning them back on at the end of the study session or during a break. This removes the temptation to constantly check your phone or messages. If you do need access to a device while studying, there are a number of blocker apps and services that can limit what you are able to access.

Tell your family and friends

Make sure people know that you are planning to study for a specific period of time. They'll understand why you may not be replying to their messages and they will help you by staying out of your way. This can also help with positive reinforcement, as you can talk to them afterwards about the successful outcomes of the revision session.

> **Tip**
> Even if you're more productive in the evening, you still need to go to bed early enough to get enough sleep.

» Useful revision techniques

Many students start their GCSE studies with little idea of how to revise effectively. There are many effective revision techniques that are worth trying. And remember, revision is a skill that needs to be learnt and then practised. It may take time to get to grips with some of these strategies, but it will be worth it if you put the effort in.

Memory aids

Before we get onto the revision techniques themselves, here are some tips on how to memorise particularly complicated information. Look out for opportunities to put these techniques into action.

Elaboration

Elaboration is where you ask new questions about what you have already learnt. In doing this you will begin to link ideas together and develop your holistic understanding of the subject. The more connections between topics your brain makes automatically, the easier you will find recalling the relevant information in the exam.

For example, if you have just consolidated your notes on the structure of the plant transport system you might challenge yourself to make a list of all the similarities and differences between the transport systems of plants and humans.

This is useful because, by answering this type of question, your brain will form links between the topics and strengthen your recall while also improving your understanding of both plant and human transport systems.

As part of elaboration you can try and link ideas to real word examples. These will develop your understanding and help you memorise key facts. For example, when revising polymer structure in Chemistry, you could relate this to examples of polymers and how they're used.

Mnemonics

Mnemonics are memory aids that use patterns of words or ideas to help you memorise facts or information. The most common type is where you create a phrase using words whose first letters match the key word or idea or you are trying to learn.

For example, living things can be classified into these taxonomic levels:

- **K**ingdom
- **C**lass
- **F**amily
- **S**pecies.
- **P**hylum
- **O**rder
- **G**enus

A mnemonic to help remember the order of these levels might be:

King **P**hilip **C**ame **O**ver **F**or **G**reat **S**amosas

Other mnemonics include rhymes, short songs and unusual visual layouts of the information you're trying to remember.

Memory palace

Memory palace is a technique that memory specialists often use to remember huge amounts of information. In this technique, you imagine a place (this could be a palace, as in the name of the technique, but it could be your home or somewhere else you're familiar with), and in this location you place certain facts in certain rooms or areas. These facts should, ideally, be associated with wherever you place them, and always stay in the same location and appear in the same order.

You may also find it helpful to 'dress' each fact up in a visual way. For example, you might imagine the information 'gravitational acceleration is $\sim 10\,m/s^2$' being 'dressed' as the apple that fell on Newton's head. You might then place this apple in the kitchen in your memory palace, 10 metres high on top of one of your cupboards.

Through the process of associating facts and their imaginary location, you are more likely to correctly recall the fact when you come to revisit the 'palace' and locations in your mind.

Key term
Holistic: When all parts of a subject are interconnected and best understood with reference to the subject as a whole.

Tip
It is helpful to use these types of questions to create linked mind maps showing the connections between topic areas.

Tip
When it comes to mnemonics, the sillier the phrase, the better – they tend to stick in your head better than everyday phrases.

Make your revision active

In order to revise effectively, you have to actually *do something* with the information. In other words, the key to effective revision is to make it active. In contrast, simply re-reading your notes is passive and is fairly ineffective in helping people retain knowledge. You need to be actively thinking about the information you are revising. This increases the chance of you remembering it and also allows you to see links between different topic areas. Developing this kind of deep, holistic understanding of the course is key to getting top marks.

Different active techniques work for different people. Try a range of activities and see which one(s) work for you. Try not to stick to one activity when you revise; using a range of activities will help maintain your interest.

> ### Key term
> Active revision: Revision where you organise and use the material you are revising. This is in contrast to passive revision, which involves activities such as reading or copying notes where you are not engaging in active thought.

Retrieval practice

Retrieval practice usually involves the following steps.

Step 1 Consolidate your notes

Step 2 Test yourself

Step 3 Check your answers

Step 4 Repeat

Step 1: Consolidate your notes

Consolidating notes means taking information from your notes and presenting it in a different form. This can be as simple as just writing out the key points of a particular topic as bullet points on a separate piece of paper. However, more effective consolidation techniques involve taking this information and turning it into a table or diagram, or perhaps being more creative and turning them into mind maps or flash cards.

Bullet point notes

Here is an example of how you might consolidate bullet point notes from a chunk of existing text.

Original text

Ultrasound waves are inaudible to humans because of their very high frequency. These waves are partially reflected at a boundary between two different media. The time taken for the reflections to echo back to a detector can be used to determine how far away this boundary is, provided we know the speed of the waves in that medium. This allows ultrasound waves to be used for both medical and industrial imaging.

Seismic waves are produced by earthquakes. Seismic P-waves are longitudinal and they travel at different speeds through solids and liquids. Seismic S-waves are transverse, so they cannot travel through a liquid. P-waves and S-waves provide evidence for the structure and size of Earth's core. The study of seismic waves provides evidence about parts of the Earth far below the surface.

Consolidated notes

- Ultrasound frequency > 20 000, so humans can't hear them
- Ultrasound reflects and the time it takes an echo to return can be used to find distance between target and source
- Ultrasound is used in medicine and industry to obtain images

- Two types of seismic wave in earthquakes: longitudinal P-waves and transverse S-waves
- P-waves can travel through solids and liquids, S-waves through solids only
- Both give information about interior structure of the Earth, e.g. size of the core

Flow diagrams

Flow diagrams are a great way to represent the steps of a process. They help you remember the steps in the right order. An example of a chemistry flow diagram, for the Haber process, is shown in Figure 4.1.

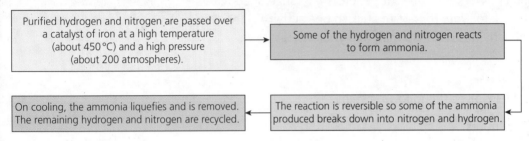

▲ Figure 4.1 The Haber process

Mind maps

Mind maps are summaries that show links between topics. Developing these links is a high order skill – it is key to developing a full and deep understanding of the specification content.

Mind maps sometimes lack detail, so are most useful to make once you have studied the topics in greater detail.

See **Elaboration** (page 76) for more information on the importance of linking ideas in active revision.

> **Key term**
>
> High order skill: A challenging skill that is difficult to master but has wide ranging benefits across subjects.

Good example of a mind map

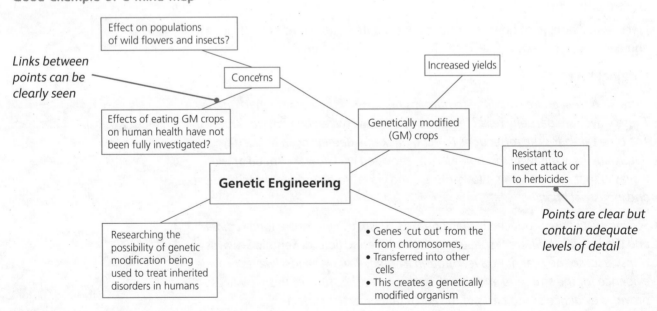

▲ Figure 4.2 Example of a good mind map

Bad example of a mind map

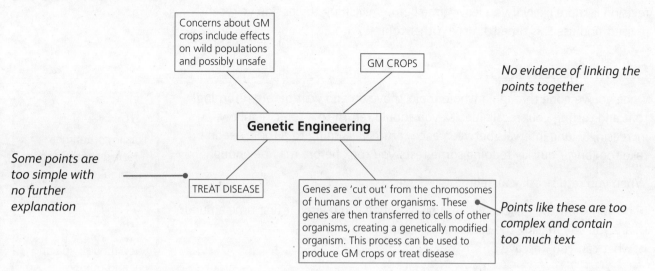

▲ Figure 4.3 Example of a bad mind map

Flash cards

Flash cards are excellent for things such as key word definitions – write a key word on one side of the card and the definition on the other.

Flash cards can also be used to summarise key points of a process or topic area.

Similar to mind maps, they should be used in conjunction with other revision methods that fully cover the detail required.

> **Tip**
> Like with mind maps, do not squeeze too much information on a flash card.

Step 2: Test yourself

There is a range of test activities you can do with the notes you've consolidated, including:

- making your own quizzes
- asking friends or family to test you
- picking flash cards randomly from a stack
- trying past exam questions

Whether you've created a test, or are asking other people to test you, it's important that you leave a decent period of time between consolidating your notes and being tested on it. Otherwise, you are not effectively testing your recall.

> **Tip**
> There are a number of different apps that are useful to help with creating quizzes. Some of these apps also allow you to share these quizzes with friends, so you can help each other out.

Step 3: Check your answers

After testing yourself, check your answers using your notes or text books. Be hard on yourself when marking answers. An answer that's *almost* right might not gain full credit in an exam. You should always strive to give the best possible answer.

If you get anything wrong, correct your answers on paper (not just in your head). And annotate your answers with anything you've missed along with additional things you could do to improve, such as using more technical language.

Step 4: Repeat

Repeat the whole process, for each topic, at regular intervals. Revisiting activities will help you memorise key aspects and ensure you learn from your previous mistakes. It is especially helpful for topics you find challenging.

When repeating, do not *immediately* revisit the same topic again. Effective revision is more likely if you leave time before revisiting topics you've recently revised, and use this time to mix in other topics.

Spacing out topics

Once you've gone through a whole topic, move on and wait before returning to it and testing your recall. Ideally, you should return to a topic regularly, increasingly long intervals between each return. Returning to a topic needn't take too long – quickly redoing some tests you took before may be enough.

When you return, ask yourself:

- do you know the topic as well as you did when you revised it first time around?
- are you still making the same mistakes?
- what can you improve on?

Identify the key areas you need to go back over.

Allow time for this revisiting process in your revision timetable. Leaving things to the last minute and trying to cram is not an effective way of revising.

Mixing up topics

Mixing up topics (covering a mix of topics during your revision timetable rather than spending long periods of time on one), is an effective revision strategy. It ties into the need to revisit topics at intervals. Mixing up and revising different areas means it's inevitable there will be a space between first revising a topic and then coming back to it a later date.

Studies have shown that, although moving onto different topics more regularly may seem difficult, it could significantly improve your revision. So it's worth persevering.

» Practise, practise, practise

Completing practice questions, particularly exam-style questions, allows you to apply your knowledge and check that your revision is working. If you're spending lots of time revising but finding you cannot answer the exam questions, then something's wrong with your revision technique and you should try a different one. Examples of practice questions can be found on pages 98–102 and online.

Practice exam questions can be approached in a number of ways.

Complete the questions using notes

This may seem a bit like cheating but it is good, active revision and will show you if there are any areas of your notes that need improving.

Complete questions on a particular topic

After revising a topic area, complete past exam questions on that topic without using your notes. If you find you get questions wrong, go back over your notes before returning to complete questions on this topic area again at a later date. Repeat this process until you are consistently answering all the questions correctly. Annotate your revision notes with points from the mark schemes. More details on the use of mark schemes can be found on pages 47–48.

> **Tip**
> This is sometimes referred to as 'Spaced Practice'.

> **Tip**
> Even though spacing out and mixing up topics are separate sub-sections here, they should be incorporated into your retrieval practice.

> **Tip**
> This is sometimes referred to as 'Interleaving'.

Complete questions on a topic you have not yet revised fully

This will show you which areas of the topic you know already and which areas you need to work on. You can then revise the topic and go back and complete the question again to check that you have successfully plugged the gaps in your knowledge.

Complete questions under exam conditions

Towards the end of your revision, when you're comfortable with the topics, complete a range of questions under timed, exam conditions. This means in silence, with no distractions and without using any notes or textbooks.

It is important to complete at least some timed activities under exam conditions. The point of this is to prepare you for the exam. Remember, if you spend time looking up answers, talking, looking at your phone and so on, you won't get an accurate idea of timings.

Always ensure you leave enough time to check back over all your answers. Students lose often lots of marks due to silly mistakes, particularly in calculations. These can be avoided by ensuring you thoroughly check all answers.

When working your way up to completing an exam under timed conditions, it can be helpful to begin with timing one or two questions to get yourself used to the speed at which you should be answering them. You can then slowly work your way up to completing full length papers in the time you would have in the real exam. Make a note of the areas where you found you were spending too long and look for ways to improve.

Effective revision is absolutely vital to success in GCSE Science. As you are studying a linear course you'll be examined on a whole two years' worth of learning. Only by revising effectively and thoroughly can you ensure you have a full and complete understanding of all the content.

> **Tip**
>
> As a guide to timings, you can work out how many marks you should be ideally gaining per minute. To do this, divide the total number of marks available by the time you have in the exam. This will help you get an idea of what questions need longer, but it is not a perfect guide as some questions will take longer than others, particularly the more complex questions that are often found towards the end of the exam paper.

5 Exam skills

Learning the content in the biology specification is only part of being successful at GCSE. You must also develop your exam skills to ensure that you get the highest marks you can. This includes being fully prepared before the exam, being aware of the types of questions and the command words used so you know what you need to do, and simple things like checking your answers.

>> General exam advice

Before the exam

Exam specifics

It is very important to be fully aware of all the specifics of your exam well in advance of the actual day. It is important that you know what exam board you are doing, so that you can read up on what to expect. Your teacher should tell you at the start of your course, but if you are unsure, be certain to ask.

You also should be aware that most exam boards have different GCSE specifications, and you need to find out which qualification you are doing, for example whether you are doing a combined science qualification like a Double or Single Award, or if you are doing three separate sciences. Some boards also do completely separate qualifications (for example OCR offers both Gateway Science and Twenty-First Century Science).

Once you know the exam board, you should download a copy of the specification. This is a free document which will be available on the exam board's website. Specifications are written for teachers so they are not always worded in the friendliest way. The good news is that you do not need to read through it all.

The types of things you need to look out for are:

- how many papers you will be sitting
- how the papers are split up (in terms of marks and content)
- how long each paper lasts
- whether there are any other assessments (for example a minority of exam boards assess practical work independently).

The subject content section of the specification is also useful for telling you everything you must know, understand and be able to do. Many revision guides, such as *My Revision Notes*, will have checklists for what you need to cover, so you can tick them off as you familiarise yourself with each area. As well as looking at the specification and paper details, it is also really helpful to look at any sample assessment materials for your exam board.

Sample assessment materials

Sample assessment materials and past exam papers are an incredibly useful resource. Past papers will show you the style of questions you can expect to be asked. For each paper, you should also check the mark scheme to see exactly

> **Tip**
>
> If you are doing GCSE Biology as opposed to combined science, make sure that you are fully aware of the extra content which is only found in GCSE Biology.

how each question is marked. You will already be familiar with how some questions are marked if you have worked through the Literacy section of this book (see page 45).

These materials can be accessed through the exam board's website, although the most recent ones may not be publicly accessible as they will be on a secure part of the site. You can ask your teacher if they can download them for you, but they may want to save them to do in class or set as homework.

Ideally, you should use the past papers for practice and revision, and then access the mark scheme after you have answered all of the questions to check how well you did.

There are other sources of questions too:

Tip
Practice exam questions can also be found on pages 98–102 and online.

- Exam questions from old versions of specifications – these are usually freely available, and there will probably be a large number of them. These can be very useful because they will cover many of the topics and skills that are assessed in the current specifications. However, you need to be careful because some of the content will have changed, and the question styles may be different too.
- Questions from other exam boards – again, these can be useful if you have already completed all of the available questions for the board you are doing. Exam papers for the recent specifications will contain more of the application-style questions that are a feature of most new specifications. As with old specifications, you need to be careful not to rely too much on these resources, and only complete questions that match the content of your specification.

Planning ahead

Exams are stressful, so it is very important to reduce stress on the day as much as possible. There are a few ways you can do this:

- Make sure that you get all the equipment you need ready in plenty of time. It might even be worth packing the night before. This means sorting out your pens, pencils, rulers, calculator, etc. Make sure you have got spares of everything, in case anything runs out or breaks during the exam.
- Make sure you know where your exam is taking place, and your seat number. This will reduce any chance of turning up at the wrong venue. It will also make it much easier when you arrive at the exam.
- Make sure you know how you are going to get to your exam, and ensure you plan to arrive in plenty of time. Getting stuck in traffic is only going to increase your anxiety and make it more difficult to perform at your best.
- Make sure you get enough sleep the night before the exam. This will improve your concentration in your exam. Late-night cramming the night before is rarely effective (see page 70 for more on effective revision tips).

During the exam

Time management

Time management in exams is vitally important. As part of your preparations, you should have already practised completing exam papers in the time given, and have an idea of a rough 'mark per minute' rate.

The following points give some further advice on time management in the exam.

- Keep an eye on the time – do not get too obsessed with the clock but make sure you are checking regularly to see if you are approximately sticking to your timings. You need to be a bit flexible as you may find that some questions take longer and some take less time, but if you start to fall behind, try and speed up.
- Do not spend too long on a tricky question – if you get to a question that you are really struggling to answer, mark it with an asterisk (*), skip it and come back to it at the end. Spending a long time on one harder question can use up valuable time that could be spent on questions you can more easily answer.
- Find time to answer every question – the only certain way of scoring zero marks on a question is by writing nothing. You should try and write an answer for every question even if you do not know where to start. Try noting down key words that apply to the topic in case it either jogs your memory or picks up a mark or two.
- Leave time to check your answers – this is very important, even if it is not a very enjoyable task. Basic marks are often lost through obvious mistakes such as missing out a keyword, putting the wrong letter down or completing part of a calculation incorrectly. By spotting these mistakes and correcting them, you can gain marks that might make all the difference.

Showing your working

Frequently, examiners complain that students do not show their working. This is probably because students often do the whole of a calculation on a calculator and do not always think to write the steps used to get to the answer. It is incredibly important to show all working because you can still be awarded some method marks even if you get the final answer wrong.

Checking your answers

As well as finding time to do a general check of the accuracy of your answers, you should do a quick check to ensure that you have spelt all words correctly. Generally, if a word is misspelt phonetically it will still be credited, but you should take care over key words and technical terms just in case.

Spelling does particularly matter where there are two or more words which are similar to each other that mean very different things. For example, mitosis and meiosis. Spelling either one of these words wrong could cost you marks.

For this reason, it is also worth making sure that your answers are clear and easy to read. While the examiner will not penalise you for messy handwriting, it is very important that they know what you have written.

Other common troublemakers

Marks in GCSE Biology are often lost needlessly. Here are some common pitfalls to avoid:

- Not answering the question – working out what to write can be one of the more challenging aspects of answering exam questions. However, you must only write down information that is relevant. Make sure you read every question in full so that you understand what the command word is asking. You will often be given useful information and guidance in the question which should also be included.
- Writing too little – sometimes a word or a sentence is enough to answer a question and get the marks. However, if a question is worth two or more

> **Tip**
>
> You will see in sample mark schemes how examiners give marks for errors carried forward (or ECF). This is a useful indicator of how you can pick up marks even when you make a mistake.

marks, you probably need to write a bit more. For example, if asked a question on the circulatory system that is worth two marks, it may be correct to say 'The heart pumps blood', but to get both marks, you probably need to write something like 'Blood is pumped out of the heart by contraction of the walls of the right and left ventricles'.

● Writing too much – you may want to write down everything that you can think of about a topic, but if it is not relevant, you will not get marks and you are just wasting time. You may even make your answer worse because the more you write, the more likely you are to say something incorrect or contradict yourself, which could lose you marks.

● Not using key words – key words, or technical terms, are of vital importance in biology. Mark schemes will often include key words that have to be in an answer in order to score a mark.

Tips

● Remember that some questions may have more than one command word.
● The number of lines given underneath the question is usually a good guide to how much you are expected to write. This is not perfect as people have different sizes of handwriting, but it is good as an estimate. The number of marks is also key – ask yourself if you have definitely included at least as many points as there are marks available.
● For maths questions involving a calculation, it is very difficult to write too much, therefore make sure you write out all of the steps.
● As part of your revision, you should be making lists of keywords and memorising them (for example using flash cards). Then you can think back over these lists in the exam and try to recall if there are any you could include.

» Understand assessment objectives

The subjects that exam boards ask about are based on their specification. This specification also sets out the types of questions that can be asked and the percentage of marks for each question type. Assessment objectives (AOs) set out how your skills and knowledge will be tested in the exam. In biology, exam questions come under one of three assessment objectives. These assessment objectives are the same in all exam boards, and are shown in the table below.

Table 5.1 Assessment objectives

Assessment objective	Approximate weighting %
AO1: Demonstrate knowledge and understanding of scientific ideas, scientific techniques and procedures.	40
AO2: Apply knowledge and understanding of scientific ideas, scientific enquiry, techniques and procedures.	40
AO3: Analyse information and ideas to interpret and evaluate, make judgements and draw conclusions, develop and improve experimental procedures.	20

AO1 questions

AO1 questions are usually based around factual recall. These questions are usually worth a small number of marks (unless you are being asked to recall a lot of separate facts).

A typical AO1 question might be as follows:

 Worked example

Prokaryotic cells are usually much smaller than eukaryotic cells. State one other difference between prokaryotes and eukaryotes. [1]

Model answer

Eukaryotic cells have genetic material enclosed in a nucleus, while the genetic material of prokaryotic cells is not enclosed in a nucleus.

You will see that these questions are literally just asking you to state information, without going into the subject matter in any more detail.

AO2 questions

AO2 questions ask you to apply your knowledge, and often focus on experimental methods and calculations. These sorts of questions can include interpreting data from graphs and tables, and using models to explain phenomena. A typical AO2 question might be as follows:

 Worked example

During a microbiology investigation in a school laboratory, inoculated agar plates were incubated at 25°C. Explain why this temperature was chosen.

Model answer

25°C is used as micro-organisms will grow at this temperature. However, it is lower than the optimum temperature for the growth of human pathogens, reducing the chance that they will grow.

AO3 questions

AO3 questions are not as common as AO1 or AO2 questions, but they are often the most challenging questions on the exam, and are therefore usually worth the most marks. These questions may require you to analyse information and use this analysis to interpret, evaluate or draw conclusions. You may also need to develop your own idea or hypothesis. AO3 questions may refer to new examples that you have not seen before, but these questions are all about applying the knowledge you will have covered in your course to a new context. A typical AO3 question might be as follows:

 Worked example

An investigation was carried out into the rate of photosynthesis by the aquatic plant *Elodea*. The rate of photosynthesis was measured by counting the number of bubbles of gas released in 5 minutes.

Explain why this may be an inaccurate method of measuring the rate of photosynthesis, and suggest an improvement.

Model answer

Bubbles are an unknown volume, and may be difficult to count accurately. An improvement would be to use a gas syringe to collect the oxygen produced. This would allow you to accurately record the volume of gas produced.

Tip

It is very important to read AO1 questions fully. While they may seem very straightforward, there could be additional details in the question. In this first worked example, the difference in size is stated in the question, which means that this cannot be given as an answer. This may seem obvious, but it is surprising how many students lose easy marks this way.

Tip

A common AO2 question will ask you to describe or explain an element of a required practical activity.

Tip

Questions that ask you to suggest an improvement to an experimental method are a common type of AO3 question.

Understanding what command words mean

You should have already come across command words in the Literacy and Revision skills sections of this book. Command words are the words and phrases used in exams that tell you how to answer a question. They will also often hint at what assessment objective they are testing. For example, words like 'State' and 'Identify' usually indicate AO1 questions; words like 'Explain' and 'Calculate' usually indicate AO2 questions; and words like 'Justify' and 'Outline' usually indicate AO3 questions.

The following is a guide to the most common command words and what they are asking you to do, with examples of what a model answer to each might look like.

> **Tip**
> At the end of the book, there is a list of command words and their meanings.

Command word: Calculate

Questions that ask you to 'Calculate' want you to use numbers or data given in the question to work out an answer.

 Worked example

Use the magnification equation below to calculate the magnification of a picture of a scorpion which appears as 21 cm long when the scorpion is actually 7 cm long.

> **Magnification = image size ÷ object size**

Model answer

> Magnification = 21 ÷ 7 = 3 times

This is a model answer because the numbers were substituted correctly into the magnification equation, and then the answer was correctly calculated. Remember to always double check all calculation questions to ensure there are no errors in your working.

> **Tip**
> It is recommended that you use a calculator when answering a 'Calculate' question. Even if it is a straightforward calculation that you can do in your head, it is a good idea to check your answer with a calculator.

Command word: Choose

The command word 'Choose' is asking you to select from a range of alternatives given in the question. Make sure that you do actually pick one of the options given.

 Worked example

Which of the following types of cell division is used to produce gametes in humans?

Choose one of the following answers:

> **mitosis, meiosis, binary fission, budding.**

Model answer

Meiosis

This is a model answer because the correct option has been selected, and there is no additional information required. Meiosis halves the number of chromosomes so that when the gametes fuse during fertilisation, the full number of chromosomes is restored.

> **Tip**
> It is important to show all your working in calculation questions. That way, if your answer is incorrect, you may still get some method marks.

Command word: Compare

In a 'Compare' question, you need to describe the similarities and/or differences between things. The key to answering 'Compare' questions is to ensure that you include comparative statements, for example, 'Plant cells have a cell wall while animal cells do not.' This is a comparative statement because it mentions two types of cell and their differences, rather than just mentioning the features of one.

 Worked example

Compare the functions of the left and right ventricles of the heart.

Model answer

The right ventricle pumps blood to the lungs while the left ventricle pumps blood to the rest of the body.

This is a model answer because it contains a comparative statement in relation to the functions of both the left and right ventricles, the difference of which is clearly stated.

Command word: Complete

In a 'Complete' question, you need to complete something that has already been started in the space provided. This could be a diagram, spaces in a sentence or spaces in a table. Make sure you write the answer in the correct places and not somewhere else.

 Worked example

Use the keywords below to complete the following statement.

The cell's .... contains .... which are made up of .... molecules.

chromosomes / nucleus / DNA / gene

Model answer

The cell's nucleus contains chromosomes which are made up of DNA molecules.

This is a model answer because all of the blank spaces have been completed correctly. This complete question contained more keywords than answer spaces, which means that one of them did not need to be used. In this case, the term 'gene' was not used – although it is part of the same topic area, it did not make sense in any of the spaces.

Command word: Define

Questions that ask you to 'Define' want you to specify the meaning of something. You will normally be asked to define a key word or term, so it is very important to learn all key word and key term definitions properly.

 Worked example

Define the term 'stem cell'.

Model answer

Stem cells are undifferentiated cells which can form many more cells of the same type, and can differentiate into certain other cells.

This is a model answer because this is a good definition of the term 'stem cell', and is better than just stating that they are undifferentiated cells. The two key terms in this answer are 'undifferentiated' and 'differentiate into'.

Command word: Describe

Questions that ask you to 'Describe' want you to recall facts, events or processes, and write about them in an accurate way. For this command word, you just need to describe, for example, there is no need to explain why something happens. See pages 48–49 for more on how to answer 'Describe' questions.

Command word: Design

Questions that ask you to 'Design' want you to set out how something will be done. This will normally be in the context of designing an experiment. See page 52 for more on how to answer 'Design' questions.

Command word: Determine

Questions that ask you to 'Determine' want you to use given data or information to obtain an answer to the question presented.

 Worked example

In an investigation into the rate of respiration, 30 cm³ of oxygen was taken in by a group of organisms in 1 hour.

Determine the rate of oxygen uptake of the organisms. Give your answer in cm³/min.

Model answer

Rate of oxygen uptake in cm³/min = 30 ÷ 60 = 0.5 cm³/min

This is a model answer because it uses the correct data from the question, and uses the right calculation to calculate the rate. To determine the rate, divide the volume of oxygen produced by the time taken. As you are asked to give the rate in cm³/min, you first need to convert the time from hours to minutes (this gives a time of 60 minutes).

Command word: Draw

Questions that ask you to 'Draw' want you to produce – or add to – a diagram. The main thing here is to ensure that your drawings are as clear and neat as possible.

 Worked example

Draw a diagram of a root hair cell which illustrates how it is adapted for its function.

Model answer

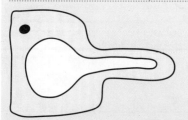

This is a model answer because it is a clear drawing which shows the large surface area of the root hair cell. The large surface area allows it to carry out its function of absorbing water and mineral ions from the soil.

Tip
Mixing up the terms 'Describe' and 'Explain' is a common mistake – make sure that you read every question carefully. Remember that 'Explain' usually requires you to go further in your answer.

Tip
Not all 'Determine' questions involve a calculation – you could be asked to give a written answer. An example of this could be determining the results of an investigation or the effect of a process.

Tip
'Draw' questions are very similar in their requirements to 'Sketch' questions (see page 96).

Command word: Estimate

Questions that ask you to 'Estimate' want you to assign an approximate value. While estimates do not have to be the exact correct value, they should be reasonably close to the actual answer. More information on estimating can be found on page 12.

More information on estimating can be found on page 12.

A Worked example

The graph below shows the results of an investigation into the effect of different concentrations of sucrose solution on the change in mass of a sample of potato.

Use the graph to estimate the concentration of sucrose which resulted in no change in mass of the potato.

Model answer

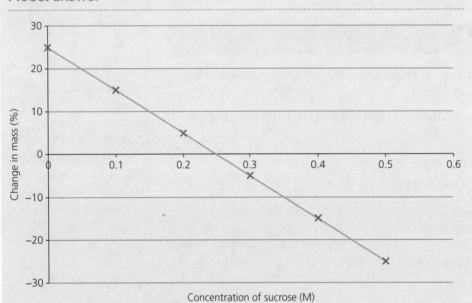

There was no change in mass at a sucrose concentration of 0.25 M.

This is a model answer because this is the point where the line of best fit crosses the *x* axis, indicating zero change in mass. This is an estimation because the answer was arrived at using the line of best fit, which is an estimate of the trend of the results.

> **Tip**
> 'Estimate' questions are not normally asked where it would be possible for you to use the information provided to calculate the exact answer. However, if you are able to and do calculate an exact answer, you will not be penalised.

Command word: Evaluate

In an 'Evaluate' question, you should use information supplied in the question, and your own knowledge, to consider evidence for and against. This command word will usually be used in longer answer questions, and you should ensure that you give points both for and against the idea you have been asked to evaluate. See page 56 for more on how to answer 'Evaluate' questions.

Command word: Explain

Questions that ask you to 'Explain' want you to make something clear, or state the reasons for something happening. Note the difference between this command word and 'Describe'. 'Explain' is *why* something is happening while 'Describe' is *what* is happening. See page 50 for more on how to answer 'Explain' questions.

Command word: Give

In a 'Give' question, only a short answer is required, such as the name of a process or structure. There is no need for an explanation or a description.

 Worked example

Rose black spot is a fungal disease which effects plants. Give two ways in which rose black spot can be spread.

Model answer

By wind and water

This is a model answer because both methods of the disease spreading are given. This is only a very short answer, but as this is a 'Give' question, no further explanation or description is required.

Command word: Identify

In an 'Identify' question, you are asked to name or otherwise characterise something. This could involve naming an organism, structure or process, or selecting from provided options, for example identifying the anomalous result in a table.

 Worked example

The diagram below shows a type of cell.

Identify this type of cell.

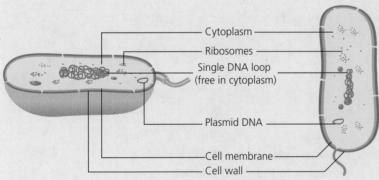

Model answer

Prokaryote cell

This is a model answer because the cell is identified correctly – the identifying feature is the fact that the cell's DNA is not inside the nucleus. Like 'Give' questions, answers to 'Identify' questions can usually be very short and to the point.

Command word: Justify

Questions that ask you to 'Justify' want you to use evidence from the information supplied to support an answer. The key with 'Justify' questions is ensuring that you fully use the information supplied in the question. See page 54 for more on how to answer 'Justify' questions.

Command word: Label

In a 'Label' question, you will be asked to provide appropriate names on a diagram. The diagram will usually have label lines pre-drawn for you to complete, but you could be asked to draw them too.

A Worked example

Label the below diagram of the eye.

Model answer

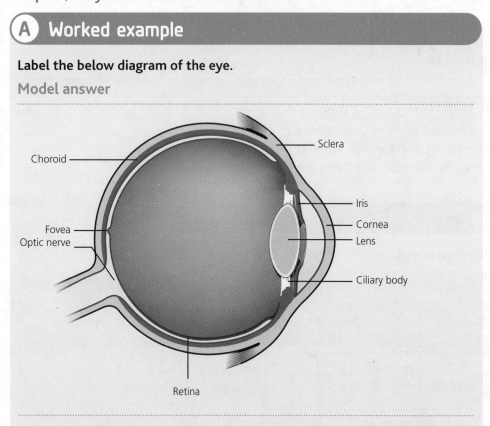

This is a model answer because all of the parts of the eye have been labelled correctly. You should ensure that all your labels are written clearly, and if you are drawing the label lines yourself, that the lines point clearly to the structure that you are labelling.

Command word: Measure

Questions that ask you to 'Measure' want you to find an item of data for a given quantity, and will normally involve using a diagram to determine a value.

Worked example

The below apparatus was used in an investigation into the effect of temperature on the rate of transpiration in a plant. At the start of the investigation, the bubble was at 10 mm on the scale. The diagram shows the apparatus after the investigation had been running for 20 minutes.

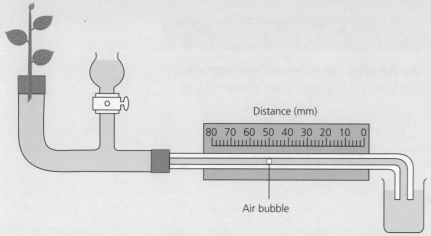

Measure the distance that the bubble has moved in 20 minutes.

Model answer

> 50 − 10 = 40 mm

This is a model answer because the value was read off the diagram correctly, and the calculation carried out to work out the total distance travelled by the bubble was worked out correctly. The bubble was at 50 mm after 20 minutes. The bubble started at 10 mm, therefore the bubble has travelled a total of 40 mm.

Command word: Name

In questions that ask you to 'Name' something, only a short answer is required – not an explanation or a description.

Worked example

In an investigation into transport in plant roots, a mineral ion was observed to move from a low concentration in the soil to a high concentration in the root hair cell.

Name the type of transport by which the mineral ion was moving.

Model answer

Active transport

This is a model answer because it is concise and correct. Often, the answer to a 'Name' question will only be a single word, phrase or sentence. Active transport is the only type of transport in which ions (or molecules) move from a low to a high concentration.

Command word: Plan

In a 'Plan' question, you will usually be required to write a method. You should write clear and concise points on how to carry out the practical investigation. See page 52 for more on how to answer 'Plan' questions.

Command word: Plot

In a 'Plot' question, you will be required to mark on a graph using data given. Be careful when plotting points or drawing bars as the examiner will check each one. For more information on plotting graphs, see pages 32–35.

A Worked example

An investigation was carried out into the effect of substrate concentration on the rate of reaction of the enzyme lipase. The results are shown in the table below.

Plot the data on a graph.

Lipid concentration (%)	Rate of reaction (1/time)
10	0.10
20	0.15
30	0.20
40	0.40
50	0.80

Model answer

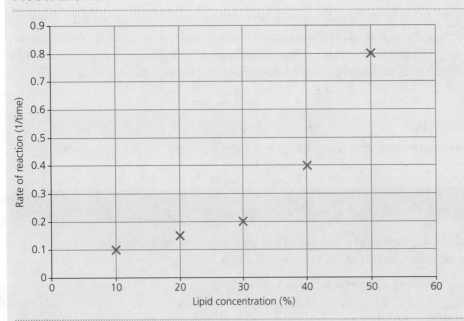

This is a model answer because the two axes are labelled and drawn correctly, and all the graph points are plotted correctly.

Tip

After plotting points on a graph, you may be asked to draw a line of best fit. This can be a straight line or a curved line.

Command word: Predict

In a 'Predict' question, you will be required to give a plausible outcome. This will involve using your scientific knowledge to give the most likely outcome of a situation. Generally, it will be quite a straightforward and obvious outcome, so there should not be a need for any strange or unusual predictions.

 Worked example

An investigation was carried out on the effect of temperature on the human enzyme pepsin. The rate of reaction on pepsin was measured at temperatures ranging from 10 °C to 50 °C. Predict how the rate of reaction of pepsin would change over this range of temperatures.

Model answer

The rate of reaction of pepsin would initially increase as temperature increased. The increase would continue until pepsin's optimum temperature – this would be around 37 °C as this is human body temperature. At the optimum temperature, the rate of reaction would be at its maximum. As the temperature increased above the optimum, the rate of reaction would decrease as the pepsin begins to denature.

This is a model answer because it fully predicts how the rate of reaction would vary over the range of temperatures given in the question. Even though the student may not have been aware of pepsin, they have used the information given in the question – particularly the fact that pepsin is a human enzyme – to make a prediction that is logical and backed up by scientific knowledge.

Command word: Show

In 'Show' questions, you are being asked provide evidence to reach a conclusion. In these types of questions, you would normally need to use information that is given in the question in your answer.

 Worked example

Pollution by fertilisers and sewage can cause decreases in the concentration of dissolved oxygen in a lake. The table below shows the effect of different dissolved oxygen concentrations (in parts per million, ppm) on fish.

Dissolved oxygen concentration	Effect on fish population
< 3 ppm	Fish cannot survive.
3–6 ppm	Fish can survive for short periods of time but cannot reproduce.
6–10 ppm	Fish can survive and reproduce.

Lake A had an average dissolved oxygen concentration of 5 ppm, while lake B had an average dissolved oxygen concentration of 7 ppm. Show how the dissolved oxygen concentrations of these two lakes can help us assess each lake's ability to support a fish population.

Model answer

Lake A is unlikely to be able to support a fish population, as the average dissolved oxygen concentration is 5 ppm and this means fish can only survive for short periods and cannot reproduce. Lake B would be able to support a fish population because it has an average dissolved oxygen concentration of 7 ppm, which means fish will be able to survive and reproduce in the lake.

This is a model answer as it uses evidence from the table in the question to reach a correct conclusion.

Command word: Sketch

Questions that ask you to 'Sketch' require you to draw something approximately. Sketches still need to be as neat and clear as possible. Sketch questions will most often involve drawing graphs.

Worked example

Use the axes below to sketch a graph to show the effect of changing concentration of carbon dioxide on the rate of photosynthesis.

Model answer

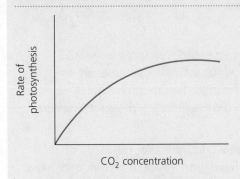

This is a model answer because the sketched line shows the trend that would be expected from changing the concentration of carbon dioxide in this investigation. The curve levels off as another limiting factor is limiting the rate of photosynthesis.

Command word: Suggest

In a 'Suggest' question, you will need to apply your knowledge and understanding to a new situation.

Worked example

An investigation was carried out into the effect of membrane thickness on diffusion of oxygen. Five different membrane thicknesses were used. Each membrane was tested once to determine the rate of diffusion of oxygen.

Suggest a method for making the results of this investigation more reliable.

Model answer

To make this investigation more reliable, you should repeat the investigation at least three times for each membrane thickness and then calculate a mean rate of diffusion of oxygen.

This is a model answer because it correctly applies a method of improving reliability to the specific example given in the question.

Command word: Use

In a 'Use' question, the answer must be based on the information given in the question. This is very important because if the information given in the question is not used, no marks can be awarded. In some cases, you may be asked to use some of your own knowledge and understanding as well.

(A) Worked example

The graph below shows the concentrations of FSH and LH during the menstrual cycle.

Use the graph to determine when ovulation will occur.

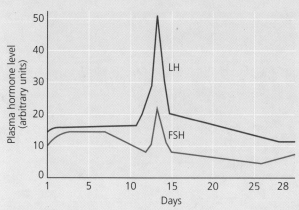

Model answer

Ovulation will occur at day 14, as this is when the concentration of LH increases and LH stimulates the release of the egg.

This is a model answer because it uses the graph correctly to determine the point at which ovulation will occur. Note the two command words used in this question.

Command word: Write

Questions that ask you to 'Write' only require a short answer, not an explanation or a description. Usually, this command word will be used when the answer has to be written in a specific place, for example in a box or a table.

Worked example

The table below gives the functions of two of the hormones found in plants. Write the names of the hormones in the appropriate boxes.

Model answer

Function of hormone in plants	Hormone
Controls cell division and ripening of fruits.	Ethene
Initiate seed germination.	Gibberellins

This is a model answer because both hormones have been written correctly in the boxes.

Put this into action

Now that you know what all the main command words mean and how to answer them, the next and most important step is to put this learning into action. The next section provides some exam-style practice questions for you to apply your knowledge, and help you prepare for the exam. Do not forget that there are also past and sample assessment materials for your specific exam board online.

6 Exam-style questions

>> Paper 1

1   The graph below shows the changes in the number of chromosomes found in a single human cell during the process of meiosis.

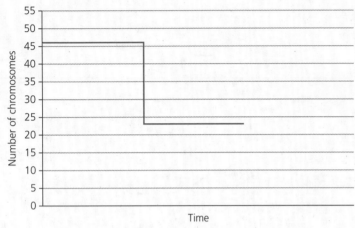

a   State what type of cells are formed by meiosis.   [1]

b   Explain the shape of the graph.   [2]

c   Explain how the change in the number of chromosomes in the cell is important for the function of this cell.   [2]

d   Use the axis to sketch a graph to show the chromosome number in a cell before and after mitosis has occurred.   [2]

2 The graph below shows how the average BMI has changed over time in the UK.

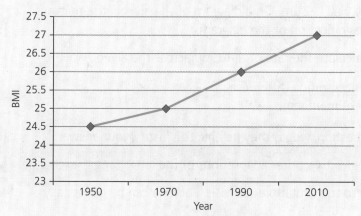

a Describe the trend shown by the graph. [1]

b Explain the trend shown by the graph. [3]

c Someone is considered overweight if their BMI is > 25.

Use the BMI equation below to calculate the mass at which a 150 cm tall person would become overweight. [3]

BMI = mass in kg ÷ (height in m)^2

3 An investigation was carried out into transport in a plant using a metabolic poison which inhibits respiration.

a When the poison was injected into the plant's stem, sucrose was observed to be no longer moving through the stem, but water continued to move up it. Explain this observation. [5]

A metabolic poison was added to a leaf. This poison prevented the stomata opening.

b After adding the metabolic poison to the leaf, water stopped travelling up the stem in the xylem. Explain why. [2]

In a 'follow-up' investigation, the movement of mineral ions was investigated.

c Injecting the metabolic poison into the stem of a plant had no effect on the movement of mineral ions. Explain this observation. [1]

4 The table below shows the thicknesses of the walls of three different blood vessels.

Blood vessel	Thickness of wall (µm)
Artery	1500.00
Vein	700.00
Capillary	0.50

a Give the thickness of the artery in standard form, and to two significant figures. [2]

b Suggest how the thickness of each of the vessels is related to its function. [3]

c Identify which of the vessels in the table are affected by coronary heart disease, and explain the impact of this disease. [2]

5 The total volume of the alveoli in a human lung is 0.002 m^3, and the total surface area of the alveoli is 100 m^2.

a Give the surface area : volume ratio of the alveoli in the lung. [2]

b A human has an average surface area of 1.8 m^2 and a volume of 0.095 m^3. Calculate the surface area : volume ratio of the human. [2]

c Use these two values to explain why humans have an internal gas exchange surface. [3]

d The thickness of the alveoli and capillary wall is 2 µm. On a diagram of the alveoli, the thickness of the wall was 15 mm. Calculate the magnification of the diagram. [3]

e A student wanted to use Fick's law to calculate the rate of diffusion across the alveoli wall.

$$\text{Rate of diffusion} \propto \frac{\text{surface area} \times \text{concentration difference}}{\text{thickness of membrane}}$$

With the information provided in this question, would they be able to? Justify your answer. [3]

f In addition to the features listed above, give two other adaptations of the lungs for gas exchange. [2]

6 Interferon is a chemical which can be used to treat multiple sclerosis. Bacteria can be genetically engineered to produce interferon.

a Explain the importance of the following enzymes in this process:

i DNA ligase [2]

ii restriction enzymes. [2]

b In the past, antibiotic resistance genes would also be inserted into the bacteria.

i Explain the function of these antibiotic resistance genes. [2]

ii Suggest a reason why antibiotic resistance genes are no longer used. [2]

7 The speed of recovery for a heart to return to its resting heart rate is a measure of fitness. Plan an investigation into the effect of the length of a period of exercise on the recovery of heart rate. [6]

8 An investigation was carried out into the effect of light intensity on the rate of photosynthesis. The results of the investigation are shown in the table below.

Distance from lamp (cm)	Rate of photosynthesis (bubbles / min)
20	20
40	15
60	8
80	3
100	2

a Plot the data on the axes below on a separate piece of graph paper. [4]

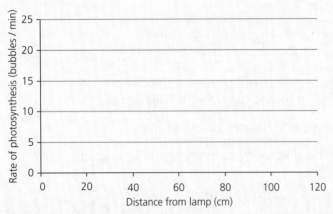

b The investigation was carried out at a constant temperature below the optimum temperature for photosynthesis.

i Sketch a line on the graph to show the effect of increasing the temperature on the results. [1]

ii Explain the shape of the line you have drawn. [2]

9 The antibiotic linezolid blocks the transfer of amino acids to the ribosome by tRNA.

   a Explain how linezolid prevents the growth of bacteria. [3]

   b In an investigation into the effect of linezolid, the clear area below was produced on a bacterial lawn.

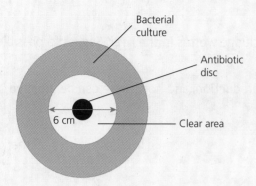

   Use the formula below to calculate the clear area produced by linezolid. Give your answer to 1 d.p. [2]

$$A = \pi r^2$$

   c Linezolid cannot be used to treat HIV. Explain why. [2]

   d Linezolid was first synthesised by scientists in the lab. Compare this discovery to the discovery of penicillin. [2]

10 The blue mussel is a marine mollusc. It is a relative of other molluscs such as snails.

   It has the Latin name *Mytilus edulis*.

   a Explain what information can be determined about the blue mussel from this name. [1]

   b The table below shows the classification of the blue mussel. Copy and complete the table. [3]

Kingdom	
	Mollusca
	Bivalvia
Order	Ostreoida

   c Name the domain that the blue mussel is classified in, giving a reason for your answer. [2]

11 The diagram below shows the food web of an aquatic ecosystem.

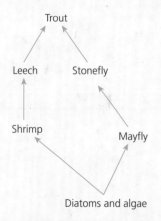

   a Predict the effect of:

     i a decline in the population of mayfly [2]

     ii an increase in the population of trout. [2]

b Identify a:

   i producer [1]

   ii primary consumer [1]

   iii secondary consumer. [1]

c A sampling activity found that there was an increase in sludge worms in the river. Suggest a possible reason for this increase. [2]

12 Describe the importance of hormones in female human reproduction, and how these can be affected by contraceptives. [6]

[Total = ... / 95 marks]

Answers

» Maths

Arithmetic and numerical computation

Expressions in decimal form (pages 6–7)

Guided questions

1 **Step 2** Root diameter to one decimal place = 0.3 cm.

2 **Step 1** The least accurate piece of apparatus is the ruler that measures to the nearest 0.1 cm.

   Step 2 Number of decimal places = 1

Practice questions

3 6.8736 g = 6.87 g to two decimal places (the 3 after the 7 means you round down).

4 One decimal place, as both other conversion efficiencies are also given to one decimal place.

Expressions in standard form (pages 7–8)

Guided questions

1 **Step 1** 500 million = 5×10^8

   Step 2 $4.2 \times 10^{-3} \times 5 \times 10^8 = 2.1 \times 10^6$

2 **Step 2** Bacterial population = $10 \times 2^{12} = 10 \times 4096$

   Bacterial population = $40960 = 4.096 \times 10^4$

Practice questions

3 $605\,000 = 6.05 \times 10^5$

4 $0.005 = 5 \times 10^{-3}$

5 Bacterial population =
   initial bacterial population $\times$ $2^{\text{number of divisions}}$

   Number of divisions = 30 ÷ 5 = 6

   $200 \times 2^6 = 12\,800$

   $12\,800 = 1.28 \times 10^4$

Fractions, percentages and ratios

Fractions and percentages (pages 9–10)

Guided questions

1 **Step 1** $\dfrac{\text{new biomass}}{\text{original biomass}} = \dfrac{1500}{2500}$

   Step 2 $= \dfrac{(1500 \div 500)}{(2500 \div 500)}$ as 500 is the largest common factor.
   $= \dfrac{3}{5}$

2 **Step 1** Efficiency of energy transfer = $52 \div 4000 \times 100$
   $= 0.013 \times 100$

   Step 2 Efficiency of energy transfer = 1.3%

Practice questions

3 **a** Energy in heather = 300 000 kJ

   Energy in grouse = 19 000 kJ

   As a fraction $= \dfrac{19\,000}{300\,000}$

   $= \dfrac{19\,000 \div 1000}{300\,000 \div 1000}$ as 1000 is the largest common factor

   $= \dfrac{19}{300}$

   As a percentage $= \dfrac{19\,000}{300\,000} \times 100 = 6.3\%$

   b Energy in grouse = 19 000 kJ

   Energy in fox = 2100 kJ

   As a fraction $= \dfrac{2100}{19\,000}$

   $= \dfrac{2100 \div 100}{19\,000 \div 100}$ as 100 is the largest common factor
   $= \dfrac{21}{190}$

   As a percentage $= \dfrac{2100}{19\,000} \times 100 = 11\%$

4 %T = %A

   30% = %A

   Therefore %A + %T = 30 + 30 = 60%

   Therefore %G + %C = 100 − 60 = 40%

   As %G = %C

   %G = 40 ÷ 2 = 20%

Ratios (pages 10–11)

Guided question

1 **Step 2**

	r	r
R	Rr	Rr
r	rr	rr

Step 3 Expected ratio = 2 Rr : 2 rr = 1 Rr : 1 rr

Therefore expected phenotype ratio
= 1 red stripe : 1 orange stripe

Practice question

2 Surface area : volume = 24 : 8

   24 : 8 = (24 ÷ 8) : (8 ÷ 8) as 8 is the largest common factor.

   = 3 : 1

   Surface area : volume = 3 : 1

Estimating results (pages 12–13)

Guided questions

1 **Step 1** Total population = 780 000 + 310 000

Step 2 Total population = 1 090 000

2 **Step 1** Round both 12 g and 19 mins to the nearest 10: 10 g and 20 mins

Step 2 Rate of reaction = $\dfrac{\text{mass of product}}{\text{time}}$

Rate of reaction = $\dfrac{10}{20}$

Rate of reaction = 0.5 g/min

Practice questions

3 Round all of the values up to 200

Mean = (200 + 200 + 200) ÷ 3

Mean = 600 ÷ 3

Mean = 200 minutes (or 3 hours, 20 minutes)

4 No, it is not the best estimate. A better estimate would be to round 3.9 to 4 rather than 3. This would instead give an estimate of:

$\dfrac{4}{6} \times 100\% = 67\%$ (to 2 d.p.)

Handling data

Using significant figures (pages 13–14)

Guided question

1 **Step 1** The first non-zero digit from the left is 4

Step 2 The second significant figure is 0

Step 3 You round up as the next digit is an 8. So: 0.040891 = 0.041 (to 2 s.f.)

Practice questions

2 5783 g = 5800 g (to 2 s.f.)

3 0.63830 mm = 0.638 mm (to 3 s.f.)

4 As the measurements are both made to 3 significant figures, this answer should also be given to 3 significant figures.

Therefore: 6.819 g/hour = 6.82 g/hour (to 3 s.f.)

Finding arithmetic means (pages 14–16)

Guided question

1 **Step 1** 15 + 19 + 21 + 18 + 23 = 96

Step 2 Mean = 96 ÷ 5 = 19 hours

Practice questions

2 Mean of B = (1500 + 1600 + 1700) ÷ 3

Mean of B = 4800 ÷ 3 = 1600

3 Mean = (350 + 400) ÷ 2

Mean = 750 ÷ 2

Mean = 375 seconds (anomalous result not taken into account)

Constructing frequency tables, bar charts and histograms

Frequency tables and bar charts (pages 16–18)

Guided question

1
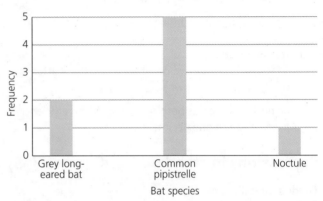

Practice questions

2
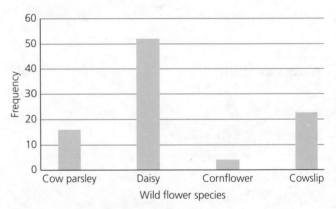

Histograms (pages 18–19)

Guided question

1
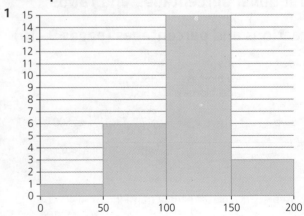

Practice question

2

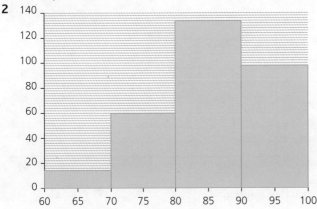

Understanding the principles of sampling (pages 19–21)

Guided questions

1 **Step 2** Population size = $(92 \times 78) \div 15$

$$= 478 \text{ (rounded to the nearest whole number)}$$

2 **Step 1** 7 quadrats contain *Digitalis* out of a total of 10 quadrats.

Step 2 Therefore, species frequency

$$= (7 \div 10) \times 100 = 70\%$$

Practice questions

3 Number of snails = (total number in first sample ×

total number in second sample)

÷ number marked in second sample

Number of snails = $(105 \times 120) \div 45$

Number of snails = $12\,600 \div 45 = 280$

4 % cover of grass = number of squares containing grass ÷

total number of squares

% cover of grass = $(15 \div 25) \times 100 = 60\%$

Simple probability (pages 21–22)

Guided question

1 **Step 1** The probability of having a boy is 0.5 each time.

Step 2 David is wrong.

Practice questions

2 Parents: Gg   Gg

Gametes: G   g   G   g

	G	g
G	GG	Gg
g	Gg	gg

Offspring 25% GG, 50% Gg, 25% gg

As only offspring with genotype gg will have yellow fruit, the probability of an offspring having yellow fruit is 25%.

3 The probability of the offspring having long fur is 0.6. This probability is not affected by the other offspring.

Understanding mean, mode and median (pages 23–24)

Guided question

1 **Step 2** Median = $(22.4 + 23.2) \div 2 = 22.8$

Practice questions

2 Median = $(4 \times 10^5 + 1 \times 10^6) \div 2 = 7 \times 10^5$

3 The mode (most common) symptom is spots on the leaves with a frequency of 3.

Using a scatter diagram to identify a correlation (pages 24–26)

Guided question

1 **Step 1** As the distance from the tree increases, the percentage cover of grass increases.

Step 2 This shows a positive correlation.

Practice questions

2 As the nitrate concentration increased, the number of trees with stunted growth decreased, there is therefore a negative correlation between nitrate concentration in the soil and number of trees with stunted growth.

3 There is no correlation between gibberellin concentration and ripeness of fruit.

4 As the concentration of blood increases, the concentration of ADH increases. There is therefore a positive correlation between the concentration of blood and the concentration of ADH.

Making order of magnitude calculations (pages 27–28)

Guided question

1 **Step 1** Image size = 150; object size = 2

Step 2 Magnification = $150 \div 2 = 75$

Practice question

2 Magnification = image size ÷ object size

Object size = image size ÷ magnification

Object size = $30 \div 340 = 0.088235 = 0.088\,\text{mm}$ (2 s.f.)

Algebra

Understanding and using algebraic symbols (pages 28–30)

Guided question

1 **Step 1** Rate of decomposition $\propto$ soil temperature

Practice questions

2 Blood pressure in arteries > blood pressure in veins

3 Rate of reaction ∝ enzyme concentration

Substituting numerical values into equations and solving (pages 30–31)

Guided question

1 **Step 1** Cardiac output = 55 × 65

Step 2 Cardiac output = 3575 cm^3/min

Practice question

2 Area of clear zone = $\pi r^2 = \pi \times 17^2$

Area of clear zone = $\pi \times 289$

Area of clear zone = 908 mm^2

Changing the subject of an equation (pages 31–32)

Guided question

1 **Step 2** Image size = 20 × 15 = 300 mm

Practice questions

2 Energy available to primary consumers = energy in primary producers – energy lost in respiration – energy lost by waste and death

Energy in primary producers = energy available to primary producers + energy lost in respiration + energy lost by waste and death

Energy in primary producers = 20 000 + 30 000 + 150 000

Energy in primary producers = 200 000 kJ

3 Number of divisions = time ÷ division rate

Number of divisions = 15 ÷ 3

Number of divisions = 5

Bacterial population = initial bacterial population × 2$^{\text{number of divisions}}$

Initial bacterial population = bacterial population ÷ 2$^{\text{number of divisions}}$

Initial bacterial population = bacterial population ÷ 2^5

Initial bacterial population = 3200 ÷ 32

Initial bacterial population = 100 bacteria

Graphs

Understanding that $y = mx + c$ represents a linear relationship (pages 32–35)

Guided question

1 **Step 1** $m = -0.5$; c = 9

Step 2 At x = 0, y = 9
At x = 10, y = 4

Step 3

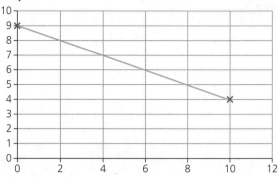

Practice question

2

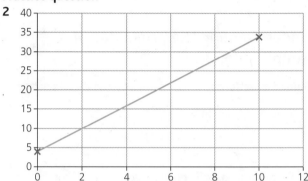

Plotting two variables from experimental or other data (pages 35–37)

Guided question

1

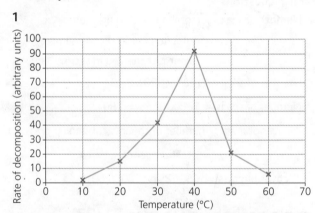

Practice question

2

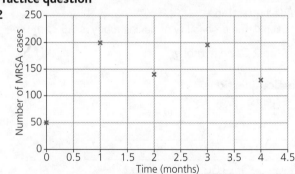

Determining the slope and intercept of a linear graph (pages 37–41)

Guided questions

1 **Step 3** Concentration of sodium chloride at which there is no change in concentration = 0.6 M

2 **Step 1** Draw triangle.

  Step 2 Change in x = 40%

   Change in y = 20 arbitrary units

  Step 3 Gradient = change in y ÷ change in x = 20 ÷ 40

  Step 4 Rate of change of rate of transpiration = 0.5

Practice questions

3 The internal concentration of the onion can be found by determining the point where there was no change in mass, as at this point the concentration inside the onion cell is equal to the external solution.

  0% change in mass = 0.53 M

  Therefore the internal concentration of the onion cell = 0.53 M

4 The rate of reaction is fastest at the start of the reaction. To find the rate of reaction, find the gradient of the line.

  First, find the gradient of the line between 0 and 30 seconds:

  Gradient = change in y ÷ change in x = 5 ÷ 30

  Gradient = 0.17

  Rate of reaction = 0.17 g/s

Geometry and trigonometry

Calculating areas, surface areas and volumes of cubes (pages 41–43)

Guided questions

1 **Step 1** Surface area of cube = 5 × 5 × 6 = 150 mm²

  Step 2 Volume of cube = 5 × 5 × 5 = 125 mm³

  Step 3 Surface area : volume = 150 : 125 = (150 ÷ 25) : (125 ÷ 25) as 25 is the largest common factor

  Surface area : volume = 6 : 5

2 **Step 1** Area of triangle = (50 × 38) ÷ 2

  Step 2 Area of triangle = 1900 ÷ 2

  Area of triangle = 950 mm²

Practice questions

3 Area of rectangle = length × width

  Area of rectangle = 700 × 400

  Area of sample = 280 000 m²

4 Area of triangle = 0.5 × (base × height)

  Area of section = 0.5 × (17 × 0.9)

  Area of section = 0.5 × 15.3

  Area of section = 7.7 mm²

5 **Cube 1**

Surface area = side length × side length × number of sides = 6 × 6 × 6

Surface area = 216 mm²

Volume = length × width × height

Volume = 6 × 6 × 6 = 216 mm³

Surface area : volume = 216 : 216 = (216 ÷ 216) : (216 ÷ 216)

Surface area : volume = 1:1

Cube 2

Surface area = side length × side length × number of sides = 4 × 4 × 6

Surface area = 96 cm²

Volume = length × width × height

Volume = 4 × 4 × 4 = 64 cm³

Surface area : volume = 96 : 64 = (96 ÷ 32) : (64 ÷ 32)

Surface area : volume = 3 : 2

As 3 : 2 is a larger surface area : volume ratio than 1 : 1, cube 2 has the largest surface area : volume ratio.

Using angular measures in degrees (page 44)

Guided question

1 **Step 2** A = 360 ÷ 6

  A = 60°

Practice question

2 A circle = 360°

  $\frac{120}{360} = \frac{1}{3}$ as 120 is the largest common factor; $\frac{1}{3}$ of the circle has been removed.

» Literacy

Extended responses: Describe (pages 48–50)

Expert commentary

1 This is a model answer that would get the full marks.

Bacteria evolve rapidly because they reproduce at a fast rate. A mutation in a strain of MRSA caused it to become antibiotic resistant. As this strain is resistant, it will have an advantage over other strains because it is not killed by antibiotics. This strain will then spread as people are not immune to it, and it cannot be treated effectively.

Doctors can help to prevent the development of new antibiotic resistant bacteria by only prescribing antibiotics for serious bacterial infections, and not for viral infections where they will have no effect. Patients must also ensure that they complete the full course of antibiotics, so that all the bacteria causing the infection are killed and none survive. Surviving bacteria could mutate and become a resistant strain. Farmers should also restrict the use of antibiotics on their animals as consumption of meat from these animals can also cause people to become immune to these antibiotics.

This answer would score the full 6 marks available because all of the information in the answer is factually correct and relevant to the question. It uses the guidance given to help create a logical structure and covers the evolution of MRSA, as well as sensible responses for doctors, farmers and patients to reduce antibiotic resistance. There are no spelling or grammatical errors.

Peer assessment

2   This answer would get a level of 1 and a mark of 2.

This is because the answer does include some correct points, such as the need for sperm and eggs to mix for fertilisation to take place and the use of FSH. However, it also contains a large number of errors. Two key mistakes are that the embryos are implanted into the mother's womb and not grown in a test tube, and also that FSH is a hormone, not an enzyme.

The answer is also not very well-structured with the use of FSH – which occurs at the start of the process – not mentioned until the end of the answer. There is also a grammatical error in the phrase 'FSH which are an enzyme' – it should be 'FSH which is an enzyme'.

Improve the answer

3   This is a model answer that would score all 6 marks:

The hormone ADH is used to control the water level in the body. When the blood becomes too concentrated, ADH is released by the pituitary gland. ADH acts on the kidney tubules and causes more water to be reabsorbed back into the blood. This is an example of negative feedback because the increase in blood concentration triggers a mechanism which causes the concentration of blood to decrease.

Extended responses: Explain (pages 50–52)

Expert commentary

1   This is a model answer that would get the full marks.

A potometer measures the rate of uptake of water by a plant. In order to investigate the effect of wind speed on the rate of transpiration, you need to first position a fan a set distance from the plant in the potometer. Before you turn the fan on, you should measure the distance travelled by the bubble in a set period of time (for example, five minutes). This information can then be used to calculate the rate of water uptake, which is approximately equal to the rate of transpiration. When carrying out the experiment, it is important to make sure that there are no other sources of air movement, such as air conditioning or a draught.

Next, turn on the fan at the slowest speed and repeat the above steps. Repeat the investigation at five different fan speeds. In order to ensure the results are repeatable, repeat the investigation three times at each fan speed, and calculate a mean rate of transpiration. Also ensure that all other variables (temperature, light intensity, etc.) are kept constant.

This is an excellent answer that would score the full 6 marks. All of the information in the answer is factually correct and only contains information which is relevant. It is a very detailed, logical answer which uses scientific terminology correctly, including explaining that the rate of water uptake is approximately equal to the rate of transpiration.

The student answered all parts of the question, including the last part which asked about how to generate repeatable results. Extended response questions can contain multiple parts, and it is important to answer all of them to gain full marks.

It is also fairly concise – rather than repeating themselves, the student uses statements such as 'repeat the above steps'. As long as it is clear to what they are referring, these types of statements are a useful way of saving time.

Peer assessment

2   This answer would get a level of 3 and a mark of 5.

This is because it is a clear, well-structured answer which covers all the main points. There is however a key mistake which is that lipids are not broken down into amino acids, but are actually broken into fatty acids and glycerol. This means that this answer scores the lowest mark in level 3. It shows the importance of ensuring that the key information in your answer is correct – even incorrectly explaining one key point can lose you marks.

Improve the answer

3   This is a model answer that would score all 6 marks:

The two groups of Drosophila *do not appear to be members of the same species. This is because when they mate, they do not produce fertile offspring. In order to be the same species, the flies would need to be able to breed so as to produce fertile offspring.*

The two groups may be different species due to changes caused by natural selection. As the groups live in different areas with different food sources, they may have adapted to the different conditions. In each case, the flies best adapted would have survived, bred and passed on their successful characteristics to their offspring. This process may have continued until the two groups of flies were so different that they could no longer breed to produce fertile offspring, and so are classed as different species.

Extended responses: Design/Plan (pages 52–53)

Expert commentary

1 This is a model answer that would get the full marks.

To test this hypothesis, first you would add a known concentration of penicillin to one disc, and a known concentration of tigecycline to another disc. Each disc containing antibiotic should have the same diameter. You would then place each disc in the centre of an agar plate to which a known volume of a specific concentration of bacterial culture had been added. You would then incubate both discs at 37°C for 24 hours.

In this time, the antibiotic will diffuse out of the disc and into the agar. A clear area will be produced where the bacteria are killed by the antibiotic. You should measure the clear area produced by each disc. Then you should repeat the whole investigation at least three times to calculate a mean clear area.

You should compare these two mean clear areas, and if the tigecycline produces a larger mean clear area than the penicillin, then this proves the hypothesis. If not, this disproves the hypothesis.

This is an excellent answer which will score all 6 marks available. The student identifies the independent variable correctly (the type of antibiotic) and states how to vary it (change the type of antibiotic on the disc).

Throughout the answer, control variables are identified correctly and controlled, for example same diameter of disc, same volume and concentration of bacterial culture, time and temperature of incubation. The reliability of the investigation is also covered by suggestions to repeat the investigation and calculate a mean clear area.

The student ends well by relating back to the question and saying how the hypothesis could be proved or disproved.

Peer assessment

2 This answer would get a level of 2 and a mark of 2.

This is because it is a reasonably clear and logical answer, but it makes no mention of using the same mass or concentration of each of the three samples of food. By not keeping this variable constant when investigating the three samples, it would not be possible to compare the results properly. The answer does score marks for identifying the test for proteins correctly (biuret) and the colour change which takes place.

Improve the answer

3 This is a model answer that would score all 6 marks:

First, set up the two tape measures to make a grid. Use a random number generator to generate co-ordinates. Place the quadrat at these co-ordinates and count how many Taraxacum *were found in the quadrat and record this number. Repeat the investigation at least ten times and calculate a mean number of* Taraxacum. *Multiply this number by 4 to give a mean number per m². You can then multiply this value by 200 to get an estimate of the population in the wasteland.*

Extended responses: Justify (pages 54–55)

Expert commentary

1 This is a model answer that would get the full marks.

Measles is a very serious disease that can be fatal. It is therefore very important to ensure that as many children as possible are vaccinated against measles, because this means they will not contract the disease themselves. By vaccinating a large proportion of young children, the vaccination also prevents measles from spreading.

Measles is a viral infection, so it cannot be treated with antibiotics. A more appropriate treatment is ensuring that the patient has enough fluids, and is resting. Measles is spread by inhaling droplets from sneezes and coughs, so if infected people are kept away from others, the infection is less likely to spread.

This is an excellent answer which would score all 6 marks available. Each of the strategies listed in the table are fully justified using the student's scientific knowledge. This includes the importance of vaccinating a large proportion of young people to prevent measles spreading, the reason why it cannot be treated with antibiotics and links keeping people away from public areas to how measles is spread.

The answer is also very well-structured, with each of these points dealt with in the order they appear in the table in the question.

Peer assessment

2 This answer would get a level of 3 and a mark of 6.

This is because it is a clear, well-structured answer which fully justifies the importance of each of the stages of the trial, including the use of a double-blind trial. The answer distinguishes between the earlier animal trials for safety and the later human trials for dose, with the structure of the answer ensuring that this difference is clear. Double-blind placebo trials are also explained well.

Improve the answer

3 This is a model answer that would score all 6 marks:

The graph shows that increasing light intensity increases the rate of photosynthesis. By increasing the light intensity in the greenhouse, the farmer will increase the amount of photosynthesis their crops are doing. This means they will have a greater growth rate and the farmer will increase their yield.

At high light intensities, the graph levels out. This is because another factor is limiting the rate of photosynthesis and increasing light intensity no longer has an effect. Temperature is an example of another limiting factor of photosynthesis. By also increasing the temperature, the rate of photosynthesis will increase to an even higher rate than if light intensity alone had been increased. This means that the farmer's actions are all scientifically justifiable.

Extended responses: Evaluate (pages 56–57)

Expert commentary

1 This is a model answer that would get the full marks.

   The conclusion is not supported by the evidence. Movement in the phloem occurs from the leaves both up and down the phloem, not just upwards. The fungus was only observed moving up from the point of infection, as the leaves below the point of infection were not affected.

   Xylem tissue transports water and mineral ions from the roots to the stems and leaves, and the movement in the xylem is only in one direction (up the plant). As the fungus seems to be moving up from the point of infection and not down, this suggests that the fungus is being transported in the xylem rather than the phloem. This would be the correct conclusion using the evidence.

   This answer scores all 6 marks available because it is thorough and details all the scientific reasons why the conclusion is unlikely to be correct, using the evidence provided in the question. The answer is also well-structured, with an initial statement on the conclusion, along with the scientific evidence for this, and then a logical alternative clearly explained.

Peer assessment

2 This answer would get a level of 2 and a mark of 4.

   This is because while it is a detailed answer, it is not focused on what the question was asking, and it fails to mention both type 1 and type 2 diabetes.

   The answer makes some attempt at evaluating the treatment by saying it could be useful when treating diabetes, and then going on to correctly explain the science behind this. However, it only refers to type 1 diabetes (although it is not named). In order to score marks in the top level, it was essential to evaluate how the treatment could be used to treat *both* types of diabetes. This meant coming to a conclusion about which type of diabetes the treatment would be suitable for (type 1 diabetes but not type 2).

Improve the answer

3 This is a model answer that would score all 6 marks:

   The addition of nitrate fertiliser would be a useful way to treat the chlorosis of the plants. Chlorosis is a condition partly due to a lack of proteins, and the plants could use the nitrates in the fertiliser to produce proteins. The nitrates would be taken into the roots by active transport and then transported in the xylem. The nitrates would be used to produce amino acids, which can then be used to synthesise proteins at the ribosomes inside the plant's cells.

Nitrate fertiliser would not treat the condition fully as chlorosis is also due to a lack of chlorophyll. Magnesium ions are required to produce chlorophyll so these ions would also need to be present in the fertiliser.

>> Working scientifically

Development of scientific thinking (pages 59–62)

1 The scientific method is the formulation, testing and modification of hypotheses by systematic observation, measurement and experimentation.

2 Charles Darwin used his own observations, experimentation and the developing knowledge of geology and fossils to develop his theory of evolution by natural selection. This differed from other older theories such as Lamarck's which stated that changes that occur during an organism's lifetime can be inherited. New evidence such as understanding the mechanisms of inheritance have led to the theory becoming widely accepted.

3 Models are important to explain and describe phenomena in an understandable way, as well as to make predictions.

4 Any two from the following, or other suitable examples:

   ● representational, such as a model of the structure of a DNA molecule
   ● mathematical, such as using equations to model bacterial growth
   ● descriptive, such as a description of the carbon cycle
   ● computational, such as a computer model to show the spread of an infectious disease in a population.

5 The impact of overfishing can be reduced through technology by using nets with large mesh sizes to allow small, young fish to escape.

6 Some people consider an embryo to be a potential life and therefore to have a right to life.

7

Hazard	Risk	Reduce risk by:
Hydrochloric acid is corrosive.	There is a risk that hydrochloric acid could come into contact with skin or eyes.	Wear safety goggles to prevent hydrochloric acid from entering eyes. If hydrochloric acid comes into contact with skin, wash affected area immediately.

8 In the peer review process, research is evaluated by other scientists to ensure that it has been carried out correctly, and that the conclusions which have been drawn from the experimental data are logical. If there are issues with the data or the conclusions, then the research is not published in scientific journals.

9 Sharing results in a class practical allows you to see if your results are consistent with those of other people, and whether they are therefore reproducible.

Experimental skills and strategies (pages 62–67)

1 A hypothesis is a proposed explanation based on limited evidence which acts as a starting point for further investigation.

2 a) i independent variable – distance of light from pondweed
      ii dependent variable – number of bubbles produced in 5 minutes
      iii two control variables – species of pondweed, mass of pondweed.

   b) Measuring the volume of gas by counting bubbles is not a very precise method of measurement. A gas syringe could be used to measure the volume of gas produced more precisely.

3 Representative data is sample data typical of the overall area or population which is being sampled.

4 Errors in methodology are due to a mistake in the planning of an experiment leading to results not being accurate or precise. Errors in carrying out the investigation are those occurring as the plan is being carried out, not due to the plan being incorrect.

5 This is important because organisms will often be stressed by being moved or put into new surroundings, and this may affect the variable you are attempting to measure. By giving the organisms time to acclimatise, they should return to their normal behaviour so that accurate measurements can then be taken.

6 The sample will not instantly reach the temperature of the water bath, so will not be at the correct temperature. Readings should only be taken once the sample has reached the temperature of the water bath.

7 Taking a number of different samples increases the chance of the results being representative.

Analysis and evaluation (pages 67–69)

1 Precision is a determination of how closely measurements cluster together. Accuracy determines how close a measurement is to the 'true' value.

2 Anomalous results are values that are very different to the rest of the results of an investigation.

3 The results of the first investigation are precise as they are closely clustered together. The more detailed second investigation produced a mean which is much lower than the values in the first experiment. This suggests the results of the first investigation are not accurate.

4 If the range of results around the mean is large then there is a high degree of uncertainty.

5 Random errors are due to results varying in unpredictable ways while systematic errors are due to

measurement results differing from the true value by a consistent amount each time (usually because of faulty apparatus).

6 Random errors can be reduced by making more measurements and calculating a mean value.

7 Ensure equipment is precise enough and experimental procedures are carried out correctly.

8 Measurements are repeatable if similar results are obtained when an investigation is repeated under the same conditions by the same investigator. Measurements are reproducible if similar results are obtained by different investigators with different equipment.

9 Repeatable results are carried out under the same conditions and by the same investigator so the same systematic error may occur each time. As reproducible results are gathered by different investigators with different equipment, it is less likely they will make the same systematic errors.

10 Large range bars indicate uncertain results as the range of results around the mean is large.

» Exam-style questions

Paper 1 (pages 98–102)

1 a) Gametes [1]

   b) The number of chromosomes halves during meiosis [1] so the daughter cell has half the number of chromosomes than the parent cell after the point meiosis has occurred [1].

   c) By changing to have half the number of chromosomes, this means that when the two gametes fuse during fertilisation [1], the cell formed has the full and correct number of chromosomes [1].

   d) Award one mark for initial correct number of chromosomes, one mark for maintaining the number of chromosomes after mitosis.

2 a) The average BMI increases over time. [1]

   b) Over time, there has been a rise in the number of people who are obese or overweight [1] due to unhealthy diets (or accept any other suitable lifestyle factor) [1]. People who are obese or overweight have a higher BMI [1].

c) BMI = mass in kg ÷ (height in m)²

150 cm = 1.5 m

Mass in kg = BMI × (height in m)²

Mass in kg = 25 × (1.5²) [1]

Mass in kg = 25 × 2.25 [1]

Mass in kg = 56.25 kg [1]

3 a) Sucrose is transported through the phloem [1] and this process requires the energy released through respiration [1], as the metabolic poison stops respiration, the transport in the phloem stops [1]. Water is transported in the xylem which are dead cells [1], so this process does not require the energy released through respiration so is not affected by the poison [1].

b) Water moves up the stem by the transpiration stream [1]. This requires water to evaporate out of the stomata, but the metabolic poison will stop the stomata opening, meaning water will not travel up the stem [1].

c) Mineral ions are transported in the xylem, which are not affected by the metabolic poison [1].

4 a) 1500 μm = 1.5×10^3 [one mark for correct significant figures, one mark for correct use of standard form.]

b) The artery has a thick wall to withstand the high pressure of blood flow [1]. Veins carry blood at lower pressure, so have thinner walls [1]. Capillaries have very thin walls to allow diffusion of gases and other substances into and out of them [1].

c) Arteries are affected by coronary heart disease [1]. As the coronary arteries become blocked, the heart does not receive oxygen [1].

5 a) Surface area : volume = 100 : 0.002 [1]
= (100 × 500) : (0.002 × 500) = 50 000 : 1 [1]

b) Surface area : volume = 1.8 : 0.1 [1]
= (1.8 ×10) : (0.1 ×10) = 18 : 1 [1]

c) The surface area : volume ratio for the alveoli is much larger than that of the human [1]. This shows that diffusion through the outer surface of the human would not be fast enough [1] to meet the needs of the human, therefore they require alveoli [1].

d) 15 mm = 15 000 μm [1].
Magnification = size of image ÷ size of object
Magnification = 15 000 ÷ 2 [1]
Magnification = 7500 [1]

e) No [1]. Surface area and thickness of diffusion membrane are given in the question, and these are required to calculate Fick's law [1]. However, concentration difference is also required, and this is not given [1].

f) The lungs have an efficient blood supply [1] and are also ventilated [1].

6 a) i DNA ligase joins [1] two sections of DNA from different organisms together [1].

ii Restriction enzymes cut DNA [1] at specific points [1].

b) i These antibiotic resistance genes are used as markers [1] to determine which bacteria have taken up the genetically engineered plasmid [1].

ii Bacteria used in genetic engineering could pass the antibiotic resistance gene to pathogenic bacteria [1] leading to the spread of antibiotic resistance [1].

7 Award marks based on the indicative content provided, up to a maximum of six marks:

Indicative content:

- Recruit participants who are same gender, age, fitness level.

- Measure heart rate before exercise to determine resting level.

- Ensure heart rate is at resting level before recording heart rate.

- Participants should exercise in the same way (for example running on the spot) for a set period of time (for example 2 minutes).

- Measure time taken to return to resting heart rate for each participant.

- Use times to calculate a mean time to return to resting heart rate.

- After a set period of rest, repeat the investigation with longer exercise periods (for example 4 minutes, 6 minutes, 8 minutes and 10 minutes).

- Compare the mean times taken to return to resting heart rate for the different periods of exercise.

8 a) Award marks as follows:

- [1] for a suitable scale on the axis.

- [1] for correctly labelled axis.

- [2] for 5 points correctly plotted.

- [−1] for each error.

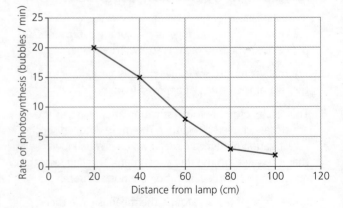

b) i [1]

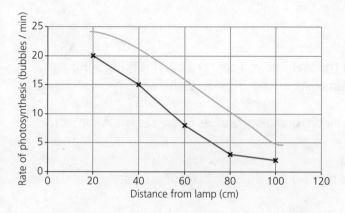

ii The rate of photosynthesis would be higher at each distance as temperature is limiting the rate of reaction [1]. Increasing the temperature will lead to a higher rate of photosynthesis [1].

9 a) Proteins are synthesised on ribosomes [1] so if the tRNA is blocked from transferring amino acids to the ribosome the amino acids will not be added to the growing protein chain [1]. This means the proteins the bacteria need for growth will not be produced [1].

b) r = diameter ÷ 2

r = 6 ÷ 2 = 3 cm

$A = \pi r^2$

$A = \pi \times 3^2$ [1]

$A = \pi \times 9 = 28.3 \, cm^2$ [1]

c) HIV is caused by a virus [1]. Viruses cannot be treated with antibiotics [1].

d) Unlike linezolid, penicillin is a natural antibiotic [1] which was discovered rather than synthesised as it is produced by the *Penicillium* mould [1].

10 a) The first word of the name is the genus of the mussel (*Mytilus*). [1]

b) Award one mark for each correct answer in bold below.

Kingdom	**Animal**
Phylum	Mollusca
Class	Bivalvia
Order	Ostreoida

c) The blue mussel is in the eukaryote domain [1] as it is an animal [1] OR it has genetic material enclosed in a nucleus [1].

11 a) i The stonefly population will decrease, [1] and the diatom and algae population will increase [1].

ii The population of leech and stonefly will decrease [1], which could lead to an increase in the shrimp and mayfly populations [1].

b) i producer – diatoms and algae [1]

ii primary consumer – shrimp or mayfly [1]

iii secondary consumer – leech or stonefly [1]

c) An increase in sludge worms would indicate that the water is polluted [1] as sludge worms are an indicator species [1].

12 Award marks based on the indicative content provided, up to a maximum of six marks:

Indicative content:

- Follicle stimulating hormone (FSH) causes the egg to mature in the ovary.

- Luteinising hormone (LH) stimulates ovulation, which is the release of the egg.

- This occurs approximately once every 28 days after puberty.

- The hormones oestrogen and progesterone are involved in maintaining the uterus lining.

- Oral contraceptives contain hormones which stop FSH production.

- This prevents eggs maturing.

- Injection, implant or skin patch of slow release progesterone.

- Progesterone inhibits the maturation and release of eggs.

Key terms

Accuracy: How close we are to the true value of a measurement.

Active revision: Revision where you organise and use the material you are revising. This is in contrast to passive revision which involves activities such as reading or copying notes where you are not engaging in active thought.

Arithmetic mean: The sum of a set of values divided by the number of values in the set – it is sometimes called the average.

Base units: The units on which the SI system is based.

Categorical data: Data that can take one of a limited number of values (or categories). Categorical data is a type of discontinuous data.

Causal relationship: The reason why one quantity is increasing (or decreasing) is that the other quantity is also increasing (or decreasing).

Common factor: A whole number that will divide into both the numerator and denominator of a fraction to give whole numbers.

Continuous data: Data that can have any value on a continuous scale, for example length in metres.

Continuous scale: A scale that has equal spaced increments.

Control variables: Variables other than the independent variable which could affect the dependent variable, and are therefore kept constant and unchanged.

Decimal places: The number of integers given after a decimal point.

Denominator: The number on the bottom of the fraction.

Dependent variable: The variable measured during an investigation.

Discontinuous data: Data that can a have a limited range of different values, for example eye colour.

Ecological: The relation of living organisms to one another and to their physical surroundings.

Ethical issues: Issues where a choice needs to be made between different options that are viewed as morally right (ethical) or wrong (unethical).

Extrapolate: Extending a graph to estimate values.

Fair test: A test in which there is one independent variable, one dependent variable and all other variables are controlled.

Fraction: A number which represents part of a whole.

Geometry: The branch of mathematics concerned with shapes and size.

High order skill: A challenging skill that is difficult to master but has wide ranging benefits across subjects.

Holistic: When all parts of a subject are interconnected and best understood with reference to the subject as a whole.

Hypotenuse: The longest side of a right-angled triangle.

Hypothesis: A proposed explanation for a phenomenon used as a starting point for further testing.

Independent variable: The variable selected to be changed by an investigator.

Intercept: The point on a graph where the line crosses one of the axes.

Leading zero: A zero before a non-zero digit, for example 0.6 has one leading zero.

Mean: The mean is a type of average.

Multiples: Large numbers of base or derived units, such as kilo- in kilogram.

Negative correlation: This occurs if one quantity tends to decrease when the other quantity increases.

No correlation: There is no relationship whatever between two quantities.

Numerator: The number on the top of the fraction.

Order of magnitude: If we write a number in standard form, the nearest power of 10 is its order of magnitude.

Origin: The start of an axes of a graph.

Outlier: A data point which is much larger or smaller than the nearest other data point.

Parallax error: A difference in the apparent value or position of an object caused by different lines of sight.

Peer review: The process by which experts in the same area of study evaluate the findings of another scientist before it is considered for inclusion in a scientific publication.

Place value: The value of a digit in a number, for example in 926, the digits have values of 900, 20 and 6 to give the number 926.

Positive correlation: This occurs if one quantity tends to increase when the other quantity increases.

Precision: Precise measurements are those where the range is small.

Quadrats: Tools for assessing the abundance of non-mobile organisms.

Ratio: A way to compare quantities; for example, three apples and four oranges are in the ratio 3:4.

Reliability: Where different people repeat the same experiment and get the same results.

Representative data: Sample data which is typical of the overall area or population being sampled.

Resolution: The fineness to which an instrument can be read.

Scatter diagram: A graph plotted between two quantities to see if there might be a relationship between them.

Scientific method: The formulation, testing and modification of hypotheses by systematic observation, measurement and experiment.

Spurious digits: Digits that make a calculated value appear more precise than the data used in the original calculation.

Submultiples: Fractions of a base unit or derived unit such as centi- in cm.

Trailing zeroes: Zeroes at the end of a number.

Trigonometry: The branch of mathematics concerned with the lengths and angles in triangles.

Command words

Calculate: Questions that ask you to 'Calculate' want you to use numbers or data given in the question to work out an answer.

Choose: The command word 'Choose' is asking you to select from a range of alternatives given in the question. Make sure that you do actually pick one of the options given.

Compare: In a 'Compare' question, you need to describe the similarities and/or differences between things. The key to answering 'Compare, questions is to ensure that you include comparative statements,

Complete: In a 'Complete' question, you need to complete something that has already been started in the space provided. This could be a diagram, spaces in a sentence or spaces in a table. Make sure you write the answer in the correct places and not somewhere else.

Define: Questions that ask you to 'Define' want you to specify the meaning of something. You will normally be asked to define a key word or term, so it is very important to learn all key word and key term definitions properly.

Describe: Questions that ask you to 'Describe' want you to recall facts, events or processes, and write about them in an accurate way. For this command word, you just need to describe, for example, there is no need to explain why something happens.

Design: Questions that ask you to 'Design' want you to set out how something will be done. This will normally be in the context of designing an experiment.

Determine: Questions that ask you to 'Determine' want you to use given data or information to obtain an answer to the question presented.

Draw: Questions that ask you to 'Draw' want you to produce – or add to – a diagram. The main thing here is to ensure that your drawings are as clear and neat as possible.

Estimate: Questions that ask you to 'Estimate' want you to assign an approximate value. While estimates do not have to be the exact correct value, they should be reasonably close to the actual answer.

Evaluate: In an 'Evaluate' question, you should use information supplied in the question, and your own knowledge, to consider evidence for and against. This command word will usually be used in longer answer questions, and you should ensure that you give points both for and against the idea you have been asked to evaluate.

Explain: Questions that ask you to 'Explain' want you to make something clear, or state the reasons for something happening.

Give: In a 'Give' question, only a short answer is required, such as the name of a process or structure. There is no need for an explanation or a description.

Identify: In an 'Identify' question, you are asked to name or otherwise characterise something.

Justify: Questions that ask you to 'Justify' want you to use evidence from the information supplied to support an answer. The key with 'Justify' questions is ensuring that you fully use the information supplied in the question.

Label: In a 'Label' question, you will be asked to provide appropriate names on a diagram. The diagram will usually have label lines pre-drawn for you to complete, but you could be asked to draw them too.

Measure: Questions that ask you to 'Measure' want you to find an item of data for a given quantity, and will normally involve using a diagram to determine a value.

Name: In questions that ask you to 'Name' something, only a short answer is required – not an explanation or a description.

Plan: In a 'Plan' question, you will usually be required to write a method. You should write clear and concise points on how to carry out the practical investigation.

Plot: In a 'Plot' question, you will be required to mark on a graph using data given. Be careful when plotting points or drawing bars as the examiner will check each one.

Predict: In a 'Predict' question, you will be required to give a plausible outcome. This will involve using your scientific knowledge to give the most likely outcome of a situation.

Show: In 'Show' questions, you are being asked provide evidence to reach a conclusion. In these types of questions, you would normally need to use information that is given in the question in your answer.

Sketch: Questions that ask you to 'Sketch' require you to draw something approximately. Sketches still need to be as neat and clear as possible. Sketch questions will most often involve drawing graphs.

Suggest: In a 'Suggest' question, you will need to apply your knowledge and understanding to a new situation.

Use: In a 'Use' question, the answer must be based on the information given in the question. This is very important because if the information given in the question is not used, no marks can be awarded. In some cases, you may be asked to use some of your own knowledge and understanding as well.

Write: Questions that ask you to 'Write' only require a short answer, not an explanation or a description. Usually, this command word will be used when the answer has to be written in a specific place, for example in a box or a table.